SUPERNATUR
The Folk Tales of North-East Wales

Richard Holland

GWASG CARREG GWALCH

ISBN: 0-86381-127-2

Illustrations and cover by Tim Pearce.
Photographs by the author.

First published in 1989 by Gwasg Carreg Gwalch.

TO MIKE —
Riding out and slaying dragons right now

CONTENTS

PREFACE

The county of Clwyd is situated in the north-east corner of Wales. Every year, thousands of people flock to the coastal holiday resorts in the county — Rhyl, Prestatyn and Colwyn Bay — and many more journey from all over the world to attend the International Eisteddfod at Llangollen. But many, many more travel straight through Clwyd to Snowdonia, most without even pausing to look about them. In so doing, they miss some of the most beautiful, and unknown countryside in Wales.

The name 'Clwyd' means 'gateway', and is an ancient one for this part of Wales. The county itself, however, is a modern one, brought into existence by the local government re-organisation of 1972. Clwyd was created from the old counties of Flintshire, Denbighshire (as far west as the Snowdonia National Park boundary), and a large northern chunk of Meirionnydd. Because my research involved the use of old documents, I have referred frequently in this book to these old counties as a means of locating towns and villages. I have also made reference to some of the districts of Clwyd, particularly Delyn, the main bulk of Flintshire, Wrexham Maelor, the most densely populated region of Clwyd, and to Maelor Saesneg, the south-easterly corner of the county, which has now been amalgamated into the Wrexham Maelor.

Clwyd is a county of varied scenery and rich history. Old Flintshire, broadly speaking, is more pastoral than Denbighshire and Meirionnydd, which are possessed of bald hills and tracts of remote moorland. Because Clwyd is a borderland, much conflict has taken place here in times gone by, and so there is much to interest the historian. The county is thick with fortifications dating from prehistoric up until Elizabethan times. In fact, it was in Clwyd (in Ruthin to be precise) that one of the most successful uprisings against English domination, under the leadership of Owain Glyndŵr, originated.

It is therefore not to be wondered at that the district should be so rich in folklore. What is remarkable, however, is that the vast majority of this folklore is virtually unknown, even to residents of the county. Many of the stories you shall read here have not seen print anywhere else for over a hundred years.

In writing down the stories for this book, I have attempted as far as possible to remain true to the oldest recorded version. All incidental detail has been included, even though it may seem obscure to the modern reader (and me), and I have by the same token kept any alien details of plot or description to a bare minimum. However, where necessary for the enjoyment of the story as a story I have included descriptive detail which might be interpreted from the original text, and I have also added some conversation. Any original lines of conversation have been used in favour of my own, however. The one exception to this rule is the final story in the book, "The Warrior Knight of the Blood Red Plume", the only textual form of which was written in 1802, and is composed in the most fluently Romantic of Romantic Gothic prose. This I have cut down. At the end of each chapter I have included a full bibliography so that the reader can chase up the original stories for him/herself.

I will not pretend that this book is complete. Despite research of a year or more, I am bound to have missed a few texts, and oral records, those tales which may still be told today but which have never been written down, will also have escaped me. But, nevertheless, it is about as complete as it could be. More importantly, however, is that it does demonstrate the glorious wealth of folklore which has resided, forgotten, in this beautiful corner of Wales.

When I first began my research I had no idea just how many stories I would discover. I certainly hadn't expected a bookful. But now, here it is: *Supernatural Clwyd; the Folk Tales of North-East Wales*. I hope you enjoy the stories presented here as much as I did when I was first introduced to them.

ACKNOWLEDGEMENTS

I would like to acknowledge all the help I have received from the Clwyd Library Service, especially Mr Dafydd Hughes, B.Sc., A.L.A., Local History Librarian, and the two Clwyd Record Offices. I would also like to thank my family and friends for all their encouragement, and for smiling politely during the times when I was boring them to tears.

KING ARTHUR IN CLWYD

Arthur, the legendary Dark Age King, is perhaps Britain's most popular folk hero. The tales of his exploits are some of the most colourful in Medieval Romance. In them he pursues quests, defeats monsters, and battles under the banner of Christianity against heathen invaders, probably Saxons, aided by his awesome Knights of the Round Table. He is in essence a Celtic hero, a Briton — that is to say, a Welshman. He lived during a time when the Celts extended from Land's End to Strathclyde. For this reason, every region in Britain claims him as its own, and his name has been associated with places as far apart as Tintagel in Cornwall, where he is said to have been born, and Arthur's Seat near Edinburgh in Scotland.

His name is also much in evidence in Clwyd. There is a Bryn Arthur (*Arthur's Hill*) at Corwen, a Ffynnon Arthur (*Arthur's Well*) at Llangollen, and two *Arthur's Cottages* (Tyddyn Arthur and Bwthyn Arthur) near Tremeirchion. There is a Crochan Arthur (*Arthur's Cauldron*) near Llangollen, and Craig Arthur (*Arthur's Crag*) is the name given to one of the many rugged limestone outcrops in the Eglwyseg Escarpment. The county possesses two *Arthur's Tables*. One of these, the Bwrdd Arthur at Llanfair Dyffryn Ceiriog, is a large round barrow. The other, the Bwrdd Arthur located in the hills above Llansannan, is quite an unusual construction. It is a rough circle of 24 indentations dug into a rock outcrop, presumably in order to resemble the Knight's seats around the Round Table, although its original purpose is a mystery.

The most pronounced topographical feature to bear Arthur's name, however, is Moel Arthur. Moel Arthur is one of the hills forming the Clwydian Range, a backbone of round-topped hills which divides the old counties of Flintshire and Denbighshire. In common with many of the peaks in the Clwydian Range, Moel

Arthur is scarred by the ramparts of a hillfort constructed many thousands of years before the birth of Christ, in the Iron Age. This hillfort was probably used as an encampment through the Roman occupation up until early Medieval times, and traditionally it is said to have been the site of King Arthur's palace, from where he kept watch over his Dark Age provinces, to the east the pastures of Delyn, to the west the richly fertile Vale of Clwyd.

It makes good sense that King Arthur would have been based in a region like Clwyd, for it is a particularly richly cultivated corner of Wales and in the Dark Ages it was prone to many skirmishes between the British lords and invading pagan Anglo-Saxon tribes. The information that has come down to us in Medieval manuscripts suggests that King Arthur was a leader highly Romanized in outlook and also a devout Christian. Clwyd was settled by a considerable population of Romans at one time. The Emperor Antoninus had his holiday villa at Bodfari, and Chester, one of the most important Roman forts, was only 15 miles or so away. Some of the earliest British saints, St Tudno for example, landed on the North Welsh coast from Ireland and made their home here. In fact, Clwyd can be seen as having been a fair melting pot of Roman and Christian impulses which might have served to influence an early British King.

Some of the earliest references to Arthur appear in a 10th Century compilation of accounts called *Historia Britonum*, which is largely attributed to a monk named Nennius. Here it is stated that Arthur fought twelve great battles in his career. Two of these may have taken place in Clwyd. An unsigned manuscript dated 1873 and residing in the Flintshire Record Office suggests that Arthur's eighth battle may have been fought at Penycloddiau, the neighbouring hillfort to Moel Arthur. *Castello Guinnion* is the name given by Nennius to the site of this battle, and it is suggested that *Guinnion* is a corruption of the word *Gwynedd*, the old name for North Wales. Penycloddiau might be called the *castellum* par excellence of North Wales, for it is the largest in the district, containing within its embankments an area exceeding 60 hectares. There is a local tradition that women and children some time in the distant past watched a great conflict from the ramparts of Penycloddiau, and this seems to support the idea. King Arthur's next great battle, the ninth, was according to Nennius undertaken at a place called *Urbe Legionis*. This may

From Moel Fama, the Clwydian Range stretches northwards. The conical summit of Moel Arthur can be seen right. Below, to the left, is the prominent hillfort of Moel-y-Gaer.

have been Chester, which was occupied during the Dark Ages and was a very important trading town for the Welsh. Another local story may support this supposition, for an old legend tells of a great army fording the River Alun near the Loggerheads to fight an invading army of Saxons at Chester.

There are also tales telling of many smaller skirmishes between Arthur and various antagonists. One of his chief adversaries was Benlli Gawr, a fierce giant who lived on Moel Fenlli, which is named after him, and which lies to the south of Moel Arthur, separated by Moel Fama. A poem dating from the Middle Ages contains a reference to a warrior who is described as having a spear of steel like "Arthur at Caer Fenlli".

On the flanks of Moel Fama is a ridge called Cefn-y-gadfa or the *Ridge of the Battlefield*, and this may be where one such conflict took place. Arthur was apparently injured in at least one of these battles, for he is said to have retired afterwards to a place called Ogof y Graig Siagus (*Cave of the Shaggy Rocks*) to lick his wounds for a time. This was apparently a huge cave of great length and at one end was a room known as "Arthur's Parlour".

The Cave of the Shaggy Rocks is now drowned beneath the lake at Ysgeifiog, which was created in the 18th Century to provide a fishing water.

Perhaps the earliest stories ever to be written about King Arthur are those which appear in Culhwch ac Olwen, a famous, and maybe the oldest, Welsh folk tale in existence. This tells of Culhwch, a young man, Arthur's cousin, who falls in love with Olwen, the daughter of a monstrous giant called Ysbaddaden. In order to prove the love he has for Olwen, Culhwch is required to perform some apparently impossible tasks, including grubbing up a hill, sowing and reaping corn in one day and hunting to death a giant boar, the Twrch Trwyth. He secretly enlists Arthur's help in these. Of particular interest is the task in which Culhwch was required to find the whereabouts of a certain Prince Mabon who had been lost in infancy. In order to do this he sought out the Ousel of Cilgwri, a magical blackbird with profound knowledge which lived in Flintshire. It helped them to find Mabon, who was being held prisoner in a castle believed to have been located at Ruabon (*Rhiwabon*), for Ruabon means *the hill of Mabon*.

It is perhaps worth underlining here that despite the fact that there is some historical documentation supporting the existence of King Arthur he is nevertheless at basis a supernatural, larger-than-life figure. After all, according to Malory's *Morte D'Arthur*, his conception was brought about directly by the magical intervention of the half-demon wizard Merlin. In other parts of Britain he was often described as being a huge giant capable of astonishing feats. Many landmarks were said to have been constructed by him. The following tale from the Loggerheads area, on the old Denbighshire/Flintshire border between Mold and Ruthin, gives a hint of the superhuman qualities often attributed to King Arthur.

Carreg Carn March Arthur

Night was just giving way to the rosy light of dawn and the mist was just beginning to rise from the vales and hollows of Delyn, when King Arthur's court was awakened by a loud and urgent hammering on the castle door. It was one of Arthur's spies who had returned with all haste from a reconnaissance of the English

Carreg Carn March Arthur rests beneath the Denbigh/Flint boundary stone at Loggerheads. The impression of "the hoof of Arthur's horse" can be seen in its centre.

Border. Breathlessly, he reported that he had seen a Saxon army massing at Chester and heading eastwards. He was probably only just ahead of it.

At once, the court was a turmoil of activity, King Arthur barking orders as his subjects scurried hither and thither preparing Caer Arthur for battle. By the time the Saxon army had climbed Moel Arthur they found waiting for them King Arthur sitting astride his magical steed, Llamrei, and brandishing Caledfwlch, his invincible sword. Forming a guard of honour behind him, in full armour, were his Knights of the Round Table. The battle which commenced was hard and furious. For miles around the countryside echoed to the clash of steel and the shouts of men. The windswept heather became stained crimson with blood.

The conflict continued from dawn to dusk. Eventually, the Saxon army began to retreat. King Arthur in the midst of battle suddenly realised that he had become cut off from his knights, and was being hedged in by the enemy. He dug his spurs into

Llamrei's flanks and the horse bolted forward. He managed to break through the enemy's ranks and set off at a gallop across the hillside. He was hotly pursued by the Saxon leader and his men. The chase led to the summit of Moel Fama, and the King was dismayed to find himself driven to the edge of a precipice. He glanced over his shoulder. The Saxons were just yards behind, their swords aloft, preparing to hack him down. Arthur leant forward and, patting his horse's neck, whispered encouragingly into its ear. The animal, realising the King's life was in danger, summoned up all its strength... and leapt into space.

Horse and rider sailed through the air and crashed to earth with such force that the steed's front hoofs left their imprint in a boulder. King Arthur and the magical horse were unharmed and returned to help rout the Saxon army.

From that day, the boulder bearing the hoofprints bore the name Carreg Carn March Arthur, meaning *The Stone of the Hoofs of Arthur's Horse*. It was once a boundary stone for the counties of Flintshire and Denbighshire and it can still be seen today beneath an elaborate 18th Century boundary marker by the side of the road leading down to the Loggerheads Country Park.

The Execution of Huail ap Caw

The son of Caw of Brydyn was an upstart. His name was Huail, he was a minor prince of small influence in Clwyd, and he was a constant source of irritation for King Arthur. He was convinced that *his* might alone would serve to protect the land from invaders, and that *he* should own the palace atop Moel Arthur. There was no doubting his prowess as a fighter and Arthur would have been pleased to have had Huail ap Caw as one of his warriors, for he was strong and agile and brave. But he was also conceited, arrogant, quick-tempered and greatly disliked in the district. And he would have nothing whatsoever to do with Arthur's court. Whilst the King spent days and nights patrolling the border, fighting with the Saxons who attempted to cross it, Huail would stay at home in his palace, feasting and bragging and thinking of new ways to antagonise his sovereign.

One year, King Arthur fell in love with a maiden from the town of Ruthin (*Rhuthun*) in Dyffryn Clwyd (*the Vale of Clwyd*). She was fair and gentle and of noble birth, and Arthur began to wish her for his wife. However, he was called away, as he was so often, to lead an army against some invading Saxons. The very next day Huail seized his chance, and he began to court the lady in the King's absence.

When the King returned, bruised and battle-weary, he went at once to Ruthin to ask for the girl's hand in marriage. There he encountered Huail. Arthur was furious. Huail's insolence had gone too far.

"If you want the girl, you must fight for her... sire," sneered Huail. He had noticed immediately King Arthur's exhausted condition and saw his opportunity to offer up a challenge. If he could defeat the King in a lawful duel, he thought, it would increase his status considerably, and Arthur could not honourably refuse.

"Very well," Arthur reluctantly agreed. "We shall meet at dawn."

"No, sire, *now*," insisted Huail. He did not want to lose this chance of fighting the King when he was at his weakest.

"Unless, of course, my lord is a coward?"

Without a word, King Arthur turned on his heel and strode out of Ruthin, Huail following, until he reached an isolated field some miles away. Arthur had not wished to make a public spectacle of the duel. He faced Huail and drew his sword.

"Until the drawing of first blood," he said.

"He who fails must cease his courtship of the lady," added Huail.

Arthur nodded his head and the duel began. They fought in bitter earnest. For a long time neither got the upper hand. Despite his weary state, Arthur was a powerful opponent, more than a match for Huail. However, his reflexes were slow. Huail succeeded in striking a lucky blow. First blood had been drawn and the duel was over.

"I am victorious!" cried Huail. Arthur leant weakly on his sword.

"I am a man of my word," he said, "the girl is yours. But I command you, as your sovereign, that you shall never reveal to anyone my humiliation."

Huail frowned. He had desired to brag about his conquest at the soonest opportunity.

"My word is law," added the King through gritted teeth. "Disobey me and I shall slay you." There was no mistaking the menace in his voice. Arthur turned and limped away.

A week or so later King Arthur received the news, at his hall at Caerwys where he was resting, of Huail ap Caw's betrothal to the beautiful Ruthin maiden. The wedding was to take place that very day. Arthur determined to be present. He decided to go in disguise.

St Peter's Square, the centre of Ruthin, was decked with flowers and many tables, groaning under the weight of rich food, had been set up on its cobbles. Huail ap Caw, already drunk, was swaggering around, laughing with his coarse friends and sycophants. He leered at his young bride-to-be, and she looked away to hide her tears. Through his drunken haze he caught sight of a shabby old woman standing on the perimeter of the square. She was staring at him with an expression of undisguised contempt. He spat in her direction and she began to limp away. Then he frowned. He was sure he recognised that limp. He strode up to the old woman and grabbed her by the shoulder. The old woman's shawl fell away — to reveal King Arthur! Huail roared with laughter.

"See, friends," he called to the assembled company, "here is our sovereign dressed in woman's clothing! And see how the poor old woman limps — a limp caused by my sword!"

The assembly fell quiet. The expression of dark fury on the King's face had been sufficient to silence them instantly. He spoke with deadly calm.

"I am a man of my word," he said. "But you have broken yours. Now you must pay the price!"

He grabbed the astonished Huail by the throat and threw him to the ground. Huail's strength was no match for that of the enraged and fully convalesced King Arthur. He was dragged, struggling vainly, across the square to one corner where sat a massive boulder. Arthur forced Huail down over the rock and unsheathed his sword. With one blow he hacked the insolent prince's head from his body.

The boulder rests in St Peter's Square still, although not in its original position. It is surrounded by railings and stands beside the black-and-white Exmewe House, which is now Ruthin's Barclays Bank. It has been named Maen Huail, or *Huail's Stone*.

A Knight's Adventure

The following story was first recorded by John Jones, a collector of ancient tales who lived at Ysgeifiog in the 17th Century. It concerns Urien Rheged, a knight who lived in King Arthur's time. The action is set at Llanferres, at a ford across the River Alun, probably the one now spanned by the old stone bridge opposite the We Three Loggerheads Inn on the road from Mold to Ruthin.

One very early morning, the neighbourhood was disturbed by a loud baying coming from the direction of the river. Urien Rheged, strolling through the countryside in search of adventure, went to investigate. The fields around the river were swathed in mist and he found them filled with packs of dogs, all facing the river and barking angrily at something which was still hidden from his view. He realised that the dogs' alarm was probably due to the presence of something very strange and otherwordly, and so he drew his sword. Gingerly, he approached the river.

Directly over the water the mist cleared and there, to Urien Rheged's astonishment, he found nothing more unusual or frightening than a woman washing clothes. He sheathed his sword and greeted the woman courteously. She looked up from her washing and smiled at him a troubled smile. Her huge eyes seemed to absorb him. Her pale, beautiful face blurred before his eyes and a terrible roaring filled his head. A strange fit suddenly overcame the knight and he became strickened with a wild and insane lust for the washing woman. Before he knew what he was doing, he had grabbed the woman, thrown her to the ground and had raped her.

Rheged crawled away in disgust and self-loathing and he buried his face in his hands. How could he, a holy Knight of the Round Table, have committed such a shameful deed against an unprotected woman? he asked himself bitterly. But he felt a cool hand on his brow and looking up saw the calm and smiling face of the woman he had ravaged.

"You were not to blame," she said. She explained that many, many years ago she had wronged the King of the Otherworld and in revenge he had placed her under a spell so that she was condemned to wander the world washing clothes until she bore a son by a Christian man. She told him that if he returned in exactly a year she would present him with the offspring of their union. Then she turned and vanished into the mist.

A year later, Urien Rheged returned to the spot by the River Alun where he had encountered the mysterious washing woman, and there found her again, bearing in her arms two infants. He took them from her and found them to be twins, a boy and a girl.

"Their names are Owain and Morfudd," the woman told him. Urien looked up from the two smiling faces to thank her, but she was nowhere to be seen.

The Burial of Arthur

Urien Rheged was not the only one of King Arthur's knights to have experienced adventure in Clwyd. Some of the action of the famous 14th Century poem, "Sir Gawain and the Green Giant", which tells of a young knight's search for a mystical, green-haired giant or *gome*, is set in the county. Some lines of the poem (in translation) tell how Gawain while on his quest kept "The Isles of Anglesey... to his left and faced across the fords by the foreshore over at Holy Head to the other side into the wilderness of Wirral where few dwelled...". There was once an important fording place across to the Wirral at Holywell, and therefore it is probably to here that the name "Holy Head" refers.

It seems that King Arthur brought his Queen, Guinevere (*Gwenhwyfar*), to live with him in Clwyd, for her presence is recorded in the name of two ancient stone crosses which used to stand in the county. One of these was at Tremeirchion, the other at Llangollen. The Croes Gwenhwyfar at Tremeirchion was once believed to possess an aura of great holiness and was a focus for pilgrims in the Middle Ages. This is a further pointer to the essentially Christian character of King Arthur's court.

According to an extremely well-researched document, *Arthur: The Clwyd Connection* by Charles Evans-Gunther, several minor characters from Arthurian legend may have found their last resting places in Clwyd. One of the King's mistresses, Garwen, is buried at Morfa Rhianedd near Llandudno and her father, Hennin Henbedd, is buried beneath a long cairn on the

The stone circle at Penbedw, near Nannerch. King Arthur's burial place?

hillfort of Dinorben near St George (*Llan Sain Siôr*), Llemenic ap Mawan, a knight who was described as one of the Three Wanderers of Arthur's Court, is buried in Tyddyn Bleiddyn tumulus near St Asaph (*Llanelwy*). The wife of Urien Rheged was named Modron, daughter of Afallwch, and it is interesting to note that the old name for the hillfort now called Moel y Gaer at Rhosesmor was Caerfallwch, or *Afallwch's Fort*. Evans-Gunther asks whether there is any connection between Caerfallwch and Ynys Afallon, which is the Welsh name for Avalon, the mysterious island where the dying King Arthur was taken after his last battle.

It is worth speculating that if all the above references from folklore and history point to the likelihood of King Arthur having lived in Clwyd, is it possible that he died here also? At the farm of Penbedw, in the valley of the River Wheeler below Moel Arthur, are five standing stones, the remains of a circle of eleven, 280 yards from which stands one large menhir. It is said that a great prince lies beneath the latter stone, and each of his warriors lie under the stones which form the circle. Could this be King Arthur and his Knights of the Round Table? The two tumuli situated nearby contain the bodies of men killed in some terrible battle fought here long ago, or so tradition informs us.

It is possible that the King was buried on Moel Arthur itself, for in a survey dated 1737 there is recorded a cairn or burial chamber with the name Cist Arthur situated somewhere on the mountain. Tantalisingly, the exact whereabouts of this cist (vault) are now unknown. There is a persistent legend in the district that hidden somewhere on Moel Arthur is a valuable treasure. Some say that this is King Arthur's magical sword Caledfwlch (known in England as *Excalibur*), but it may also refer to Arthur's grave, for he would certainly have been interred with considerable riches as would befit his high rank. In fact, gold was mined on the slopes of Moel Arthur until quite recent times, and the lodes would presumably have been very rich way back in the Dark Ages.

The site of the treasure was said to be illuminated by a pale light shining on the hillside at midnight. As a result, many hopeful prospectors spent the hours of darkness roaming the mountain in search of it, armed with picks and shovels. One or two actually claimed to have found it. However, no-one was able to carry it away, for it was protected by a supernatural agent. When a group of treasure hunters set off up the hill one fine day last century, an old woman who lived in a cottage in the valley sadly shook her head and commented:

"Why, then, we shall have a storm upon us before long." She was proved correct, for as soon as the first spade was plunged into the soil up on Moel Arthur, menacing black clouds rolled down from the previously clear sky and a sudden violent gale blew up. Thunder roared and flashes of lightning flared around the hills. Through the heavy rain that quickly followed a party of wet-through, thoroughly demoralised and rather frightened men trudged their weary way past the old woman's cottage. The sudden storm had driven them away. On another occasion, one man claimed to have succeeded in digging down to a huge oak treasure chest somewhere on the mountain, and had managed to touch the iron ring attached to it, before the fierce squalls of wind and driving rain that had sprung up from nowhere on his discovery forced him back down the hill.

Although these supernatural storms were offputting enough to most would-be treasure seekers, more daunting still was the treasure's guardian, a terrible apparition which patrolled Moel Arthur after dark. This was the Grey Lady, a statuesque figure with a fearful expression and eyes which could frighten to death anyone she found on the mountain. There is a story which tells of a poor local man, almost destitute in his poverty, who became lost one evening on the mountain while returning home from a desperate search for work elsewhere. Through the gloom he perceived a tall, imposing silhouette floating towards him. His breath caught in his throat and he shook with fear. It was the Grey Lady! Quickly, he looked at his feet to avoid her fatal gaze and started to mutter a prayer. The Grey Lady glowered down upon him.

"What do you here?" she demanded.

"Please... ma'am," he stuttered. "I am lost."

There was a long pause.

"Hold out your hand," the Grey Lady told him. Trembling, he did so and the strange ghost dropped three dry peas into his upturned palm.

"Now go home," the Grey Lady commanded, and vanished. When the poor man did eventually find his way back to his tiny cottage in the valley, he found that the peas had turned into pure gold.

It is unknown who the Grey Lady may have been, but one thing is certain: it must have been a very great treasure indeed buried on Moel Arthur to have warranted such a powerful guardian. Perhaps it is the burial place of Britain's most celebrated King, Arthur, which she is charged to protect.

King Arthur in Clwyd — Bibliography

Geoffrey Ashe, *A Guide Book to Arthurian Britain* (Longman Travellers Series).

W. Lewis Jones, *King Arthur in History and Legend* (Cambridge University Press 1911).

Tony Roberts, *Myths and Legends of Wales* (Abercastle Publications 1979).

Rev. Elias Owen, *Old Stone Crosses in the Vale of Clwyd* (London and Oswestry & Wrexham 1886).

S.J. Coleman, *Lore and Legend of Flintshire* (Folklore Academy 1956).

J.B. Lewis M.A., *An Account of the Penbedw Papers in the Flintshire Records Office* (Flintshire Historical Transactions).

Charles V. Evans-Gunter, *Arthur: The Clwyd Connection*.

MONSTERS

The heraldic badge of Wales is the *Ddraig Goch*, or Red Dragon. The origin of this symbol is explained in the ancient tale of Vortigern, who was a British king living before the birth of King Arthur. At Dinas Emrys in Snowdonia King Vortigern had attempted to build a palace, but before it was half finished earth tremors would suddenly raze it to the ground. A youthful Merlin, King Arthur's wizard, told Vortigern that the earth tremors were caused by the thrashings of two dragons which were locked in deadly combat deep below the ground. Vortigern's men excavated Dinas Emrys until they reached an extensive cavern, at the bottom of which there lay a lake. The surface of the lake was suddenly thrown into a turmoil and two monstrous serpents emerged, each with its deadly jaws grasping the other's tail. The serpents were of two different colours. One was white, the other red. Merlin told the astonished Vortigern that the dragons were symbols of the struggle between the Welsh and Saxon nations. The white dragon represented England, the red dragon represented Wales. The battle between them would continue for many centuries, until one was eventually vanquished. From that day, the Red Dragon has become the national symbol of Wales.

The above is quite a well-known legend. Less well-known is the local story regarding England's patron saint, St George. St George was canonized not only in recognition of his virtuous character and pious Christianity but also of his courageous slaying of a horrible dragon. Most of the history books, however, do not state where St George slew his dragon. In fact, it was in Clwyd. The little village of St George, which is midway between St Asaph (*Llanelwy*) and Abergele, was named after the saint, because it was here that the deed took place. The conflict with the dragon was so furious that some hoof marks, caused by the stamping of St George's horse, were left imprinted in a boulder in the village, as evidence of the holy victory.

St George's dragon was not the only one to have plagued Clwyd. One haunted the old castle at Denbigh (*Dinbych*). Another lurked around the countryside south of the Berwyn Mountains. In addition, there were also "lesser" serpents, according to Marie Tevelyan in her book *Folklore and Folk Stories of Wales*. These frequented the remote valleys and gullies of the Berwyn Mountains themselves. I'm not quite sure what dimensions these "lesser" serpents took, for a full-sized dragon could be as long as the tallest pine tree. Perhaps the giant snake which attacked a carter at Overton was an example of the breed.

One year in the early 19th Century, there was a news report of a "huge snake" being encountered at the village of Overton in Wrexham Maelor. It had leapt out of a hedge and attacked a team of horses carrying a cart of coal near the bridge. With considerable difficulty the carter succeeded in killing it, and he draped it over his cart. The carcass was so long that its head reached the ground in front and its tail dragged along behind!

Another kind of monster, bearing some kinship with the dragons, was the *Ceffyl Dŵr*, or Water Horse. This terrifying beast had its home at the bottom of pools of still water, from which it would emerge at night to leap on the backs of anyone walking past. According to Marie Trevelyan, a *Ceffyl Dŵr* lived in the Vale of Clwyd. It had the shape of an enormous frog and if it captured some unlucky wayfarer, it would hold them tight in "a fiendish embrace".

Stories abound throughout the world of races of hirsute men who live in the depths of forests and are seldom seen. In Tibet they are called Yeti, in Africa Nandi Bears and in America they are the Bigfoot or Sasquatch. In English folklore they were called Woodwoses. A few of these mysterious Troglodytes seem to have lived in Wales, too. The representation of one is carved into a pillar near the altar of Mold (*Yr Wyddgrug*) Parish Church. He is a jovial little figure, covered in hair, dancing among some vine leaves. More frightening was the monster which haunted a little coppice of ancient woodland at Gloddaeth, near Llandudno. It was twice as tall as a man, and it had glowing red eyes and a coat of shaggy black hair. At night it could be heard creeping around the wood letting out an eerie, high-pitched wail, like the cry of a drowning man. In Clwyd, something similar was encountered by a man in Bylchau in Denbighshire. He had been gathering nuts on a Sunday when he should have been at church. However, when he reached his hand into a particularly nut-laden bush for some fruit, another, larger and hairer, hand reached out for his! Screaming with terror, the man ran back down the hill straight to the church, and he never wasted another Sabbath nut collecting again.

By far the commonest monsters to have once lived in Clwyd, however, are the giants. Apart from the natural giants born amongst men, like the heroic David Salusbury whom we shall come across in the Denbigh Dragon story, the giants were a distinct and ancient race. Some were well-natured. Most were bad-tempered and fierce. A few ate people. Almost all of them were stupid. But the one thing they had in common was their monstrous size. Some were big enough to carry pine trees over their shoulders like clubs, while others were so huge that they could wade across the Irish Sea.

King Brân the Blessed, perhaps the most important figure in the folk tales of Wales, was a giant, and he also lived in Clwyd. It is his story which opens the tales in this chapter.

Brân the Blessed

One of the most enigmatic places in Clwyd is Dinas Brân. The ruins of a 13th Century castle, Dinas Brân stands proud upon a steep hill which overlooks one of the most beautiful scenes in Wales, the Vale of Llangollen. The castle was built on the site of a much earlier fortress, and a settlement has probably been here for thousands of years. Dinas Brân means *The City of Brân* and is named after Brân the Blessed, who was a giant and also, according to The Mabinogion, that famous collection of ancient Welsh tales, one of the first Kings of Britain. In early Welsh literature, Brân the Blessed is an even more important figure than his successor, King Arthur. Brân means *The Raven* and Dinas Brân is sometimes known as Crow Castle. It may be assumed that Brân ruled Britain from Dinas Brân, since allusions in Medieval Welsh poetry reveal that North-Eastern Wales was once known as the land of Brân. His name lives on in other nearby place names, such as Gorsedd Frân (*The Throne of Brân*) and Llyn Brân (*The Lake of Brân*).

Brân had a daughter called Branwen and he ruled with the help of his brother Manawydan. Their story as told in The

Mabinogion is quite a tragic one.

One day the King of Ireland arrived in Wales with an entourage to ask King Brân for the hand of his daughter in marriage. Since such a union would help preserve peace between the two nations, Branwen consented, and her father organised a wedding feast. During the course of the festivities, however, a thwarted suitor of Branwen's made trouble and insulted the King of Ireland. Brân was horrified that a guest in his house should suffer insult, and the Irish King himself affected such offence that it seemed that it might be war.

However, Brân managed to calm him by means of a formal apology, and he requested that the King choose for himself any gift it was in his power to grant. The King of Ireland chose Brân's magic cauldron. A murmur of dismay rose from the Welsh courtiers on hearing this. The magic cauldron was Brân's most precious possession. It had the ability to bring back to life any warrior slain in battle. Reluctant though he was, Brân was honour bound to part with it, and the very next day the King of Ireland's fleet sailed away, with the magic cauldron and with Branwen.

As soon as the fleet was safely away from Wales, and had docked in Ireland, the King began to abuse Branwen terribly. He stripped her of all her noble rights and forced her to work in the kitchen as a maid. Many months passed and no word reached Wales of Branwen's plight. However, being a royal princess, and made of stern stuff, the poor girl bore up with fortitude and did not lose hope. Very patiently she trained a starling to carry a message across the sea to her father's court, and then released it. When Brân received the message he was outraged and at once informed Manawydan of the shocking news. Together they mustered an army, and at once set sail for Ireland. Brân, being a giant, was too big to fit into one of the ships, and so he led the fleet by wading across the channel.

They found the King of Ireland and his army waiting on the other side of the Shannon River, and battle immediately commenced. The Welsh army was much more accomplished than the Irish, and after the first day of battle they seemed to have got the upper hand. Unfortunately, Brân's gift to the King of Ireland, his magic cauldron, made this advantage only temporary. At nightfall, when both armies removed their dead and dying from the field, the Irish corpses were placed one by

The glorious Vale of Llangollen, once known as "the land of Brân".

The enigmatic ruins of Dinas Brân.

one into the cauldron and immediately they sprang to life, warriors fresh for more fighting. From then on, with each successive battle, the Welsh army weakened. It mattered not how many of the Irish were slaughtered, for with each new day their numbers were the same as they had been at the onset.

Eventually, there were only seven survivors on the Welsh side, including Manawydan and King Brân. Brân's huge size and enormous strength had served to keep the Irish army at bay long enough to allow Branwen to escape her confinement. However, just as she reached her father's side, a poisoned spear was thrown into his foot, and he collapsed, mortally wounded. Breathlessly, life ebbing from his body, Brân commanded his followers to strike his head from his body.

"Carry it with you," he told them, "to the White Mound at London. There bury it facing out to sea. For so long as it remains there it shall preserve Britain from invasion."

When the King of Ireland saw the Welsh survivors beheading their own king, he put up his hand and the battle ceased. He allowed the seven survivors to sail away with Brân's head. The head, however, had remained alive, and to the survivors' amazement, it talked to them. Unfortunately, Branwen, heartbroken by the ruin and the death which she had inadvertently helped cause, would not be comforted by it, and when the ship landed at Anglesey (*Ynys Môn*) near the mouth of the River Alaw, she disembarked, turned her face to gaze across the sea to Ireland, and there died from her remorse. A funeral pyre was lit by the mouth of the river and her body was sadly consigned to the flames by her uncle. This region of Anglesey became known as "Branwen's Island", and in 1813 a tumulus here was dug into revealing a simple Bronze age burial, the last resting place of the daughter of Brân.

The ship set sail once again and Brân's severed head continued to converse with Manawydan and his small crew. It also magically supplied the men with unlimited quantities of food and drink to sustain them. This was just as well, for the head's presence had the effect of suspending time, so that in the end the voyage to London took eighty years. However, throughout that time, not one member of the crew discernably aged. On eventually reaching London Brân's head was solemnly buried beneath the White Mound as instructed so that it gazed out over the English Channel, magically preserving the country from foreign invasion.

The White Mound has since been identified as Tower Hill, one of the earliest inhabited sites in Britain, and where now stands the Tower of London, of course. It is interesting to note that a memory of this old story continues into our own day in the form of the superstition regarding the ravens of the Tower. It is said that should ever the pet ravens kept at the Tower fly away, Britain will cease to be... and the raven is the symbol of Brân the Blessed. Brân's head remained under the White Mound for several centuries, until it was exhumed by King Arthur, foolishly avowing that no stronger protection was needed for Britain than himself. Unfortunately, he was proven wrong, for shortly after he had done so, the Angles and the Saxons began to invade.

Hoard of the Devil Giant

Legend and mystery associated with Dinas Brân does not end with the death of Brân the Blessed. The castle is linked with the story of the quest for the Holy Grail. The Holy Grail was the chalice used by Christ at the Last Supper and, so the legend says, it was brought to the British Isles during the Dark Ages by an early saint, Joseph of Arimathea, who founded the ancient church of Glastonbury in Somerset. It became the symbol of absolute purity and the focus for a series of quests undertaken by King Arthur's Knights of the Round Table. In Arthurian Romance, the keeper of the Holy Grail is named *Bron*, and Malory in his *Morte D'Arthur* names the castle in which it was kept *Corbin*. Malory had taken his stories from early French manuscripts, and *corbin* is an old French word meaning crow or raven. *Corbin* is therefore translatable as *Crow Castle*. And *Crow Castle* is another name for Dinas Brân.

One of Clwyd's most persistant legends is that of a fabulous treasure lying buried somewhere deep beneath the castle on Dinas Brân. It is said that the finding of the treasure will be by a boy who has a white dog with silver eyes which can see the wind. Quite what form the treasure takes seems uncertain. Perhaps it is the Holy Grail. Some say that it is a golden harp. Others say that it is a magical horn of plenty. Most imaginatively, it has been described as a treasure of:

"...oxen, cows, swans, peacocks, horses, and all other animals of fine gold, and there was a golden bull which told of events which were to come."

This description was recorded in the 1896 edition of *Byegones*, an old historical magazine for Wales and the Border. A few years later, *Byegones* also recorded the local legend that the hoard was guarded by "a giant raven", which is surely another folk memory of Brân the Blessed. However, there is one point on which the legends agree: the treasure was not inhumed by Brân. It was the property of another giant altogether, a giant called Goemagog. According to an old French poem, Goemagog lived in the ruins on Dinas Brân in the 11th Century. This poem is called *Fouke Fitz Warin*, and it tells an extraordinary story.

It was a few years after the Norman Conquest of England and King William I was touring his newly-acquired nation with a company of some of his best knights. He passed into Wales just north of Oswestry and soon reached the Vale of Llangollen. Here he saw, towering above him on the crown of a steep hill, the walls of a great city, apparently deserted.

"What is that place?" he asked his Welsh guide.

"That is Chastiel Brân, sire," he was informed.

"But why is it deserted?" he asked. The guide shuddered and crossed himself and cast his eyes up to the lofty ruins warily. He told the king that although Chastiel Brân had once been a fine palace it had lately become the home of a giant called Goemagog, who "so harried the place that no-one dared to live there". He went on to say that Goemagog had once seemed peaceable but in recent months had become a fierce, fire-breathing monster and all the local populace went in fear of it.

King William was shocked by the story, and he determined that something should be done about it. He had in his company his best knight, a man named Payn Peverel. He ordered Payn Peverel to free the countryside by climbing the mountain and vanquishing the monster.

"Certainly sire, consider the deed as good as done!" vowed the valiant Peverel (who was everything one would expect from a knight in a story such as this). He set off boldly up the hill.

It was nearly dark by the time Payn Peverel reached the outer defensive wall of the castle, and he felt very tired from his long climb. He leant wearily upon his huge, double-bladed sword and unhitched his heavy shield. He mopped his brow. All was quiet.

A gentle breeze caressed the grassy slope and a few black crows drifted silently down the vale. Peverel shivered involuntarily. There was something unnerving about the quiet. He took a deep breath, picked up his sword and shield and cautiously entered the city.

Of Goemagog there was no sign. The place was quite deserted. A smell of death hung in the air. Suddenly, a flash of lightning burst across the sky and a loud clap of thunder made Peverel jump. Then a powerful wind sprang up from nowhere and roared around the city, buffeting the knight from side to side. Heavy drops of rain began to fall as black clouds closed in around the hill. The thunder rumbled and echoed around the empty ruins and more flashes of lightning briefly illuminated the scene. Suddenly, Peverel gave a cry of alarm. Silhouetted against the last burst of lightning, he had seen a huge and shaggy shape rising up before him!

Peverel staggered backwards and he raised his sword. The huge shape came closer and was suddenly illuminated by lightning. Towering before him was the giant, Goemagog, more horrible in aspect than he could ever have imagined. Its heavy, brutish features were like those of a cadaver. Its eyes were rolled up in its head and here and there portions of flesh hung away from the bone, which gleamed palely beneath. In its swollen face its teeth grinned obscenely, and it reached out its huge paws towards the terrified knight...

Peverel cried out with disgust and lashed at the monstrosity with his sword. He backed out great chunks of flesh, but the Giant seemed unaffected. It roared with rage and blew a great jet of flame from its mouth. Peverel dodged behind a pillar, his hair and eyebrows singed. With one blow, the giant smashed the pillar to the ground. Despairing, Peverel threw his sword at the monster, but it stuck in its belly with no apparent effect. It spat more flame from its mouth, and Peverel held up his shield to protect himself...

With a yell of anguish the giant stumbled back. Something about Peverel's shield seemed to be causing it pain. Holding it at arm's length, the knight waved his shield at the giant. The monster roared and fell backwards, covering its face with its hands. Peverel felt confused. A brief moment ago he had been at the giant's mercy. What had caused this change in his fortunes? Then he remembered that the device on his shield was a crucifix, a bold red cross. The holy symbol had vanquished the giant's evil, and had rendered it powerless!

Peverel gave thanks to heaven and then strode up to the cowering giant. He pressed his shield down upon it and it shrieked with agony.

"Have mercy!" it begged.

"Very well," said Peverel, "provided that you explain to me your reasons for haunting this place, and that afterwards you leave at once and never return. First, tell me, are you Goemagog?"

"No," the giant replied.

It told him that in fact it was a devil inhabiting the giant's body. Goemagog had died just after burying his fabulous treasure beneath the castle. The devil had taken over his corpse, and re-animated it in the hope of securing the treasure for itself. In this it had so far been unsuccessful. Peverel lowered his shield and the devil leapt from the dead giant's mouth. It went screaming away through the night sky, and did not return.

Payn Peverel wearily descended the mountain and told the king his fantastic story. Immediately, a search was organised to try and discover the fabulous treasure buried by the giant. But it was a failure. Centuries have passed and Dinas Brân is now a hollow ruin, but the treasure still remains unfound.

Benlli Gawr

Moel Fenlli means *The Hill of Benlli*. It is an imposing hill, black with heather, and its crown is prominently furrowed by the ramparts of a prehistoric hillfort. The fort was built to guard over the pass of Bwlch Pen Barras, once one of the most important routes through the Clwydian Range. Many centuries ago, it served as the court of a Celtic prince named Benlli Gawr, or *Benlli the Giant*.

Benlli Gawr was a terrible tyrant. His monstrous cruelty was matched only by his monstrous size. He ruled over the province of Iâl, a district of rich farmland and pretty meadows, whose natives he kept in slavery and controlled with fear. He was possessed of enormous pride of ambition, and this brought him into conflict with all the neighbouring princes, including King

Foel Fenlli, with the ramparts of its ancient hillfort clearly marked on the left hand side of its summit, looms above the pass of Bwlch Pen Barras.

Arthur, who lived a few miles to the north on Moel Arthur. His court was the refuge of every bandit in Wales and it was infamous for its evil ways.

One year, in an attempt to gain control of Clwyd, Benlli had sided with an army of savage Picts which was invading Wales from the North Countries. Bravely, a small band of Christians had mustered together at Mold in the hope of repelling this army. Although their numbers were small their will was strong, for their leader was St Garmon (also called St Germanus), a devout and powerful saint who led them in prayer before the battle. He directed his men to spread themselves out and hide around the slopes overlooking a hollow now called Maes Garmon (*Garmon's Field*). There they waited for his signal. When the Pictish army entered this hollow, St Garmon jumped up. At once, all the Christians leapt to their feet, and they clashed their weapons together furiously, crying in unison "Alleluia!"

The Picts were so startled by the loud din and the Christians' sudden appearance that they imagined bearing down upon them more numbers than there actually were. With one accord they downed weapons and fled. Benlli fled, too. However, his presence had not gone unnoticed by St Garmon.

A few days after the Alleluia Battle (as it has become known), St Garmon decided to pay Caer Fenlli a visit, in the hope of converting some of its inmates to the Christian faith. He climbed up to the top of Bwlch Pen Barras and hammered on the fortress' heavy door. Benlli peered over the tall pallisade walls to see who it was, and then ducked down rapidly. Benlli the Giant was frightened of few men, but St Garmon was one of them. He dared not face the holy man himself, and so, by way of an insult, he decided to send his humblest servant to meet him at the door. This was Cadell, his swineherd. Cadell was, in fact, a good man, the only one in Caer Fenlli, and so, when he answered the door to the saint, he was as polite as possible.

"I am afraid I am bidden by my master to ask you to leave," he said. St Garmon nodded his head. He shouted through the open doorway that should anyone wish to leave the evil den and become baptised into the Christian faith, he was at their service. This was met with jeers and catcalls from the sinful courtiers within, and loud braying laughter from Benlli (who was hiding somewhere at the back). Cadell, however, quietly closed the door behind him and bowed low before the holy saint.

"Thank you, I would like to," he said. "Please allow me to offer you my humble hospitality."

He led St Garmon to a tiny stone cottage in the valley and he killed his prize animal, a fatted calf, to feed him. Then he sat down and he wept, for he knew that the next day he was sure to be executed by Benlli for his treachery. But St Garmon spoke words of comfort to him, and there and then baptised him.

"Fear not, for no harm will come to you," he vowed. Then he begged his leave and retired alone. All night he prayed to the Almighty that Cadell's goodness should not go unrewarded and that retribution should fall upon Benlli and his evil court.

The first thing that greeted Cadell's eyes, as he threw back the shutters to let in the morning light, was his prize calf, which they had eaten just the night before, outside, alive and well and grazing contentedly by its mother. He gaped in amazement, and ran outside to convince himself that he was not hallucinating. Then he cast his eyes heavenwards to offer thanks.

He blinked. There were two suns in the sky! One of the "suns" was growing larger and larger, and Cadell realised that it was falling to earth. He ran inside and ducked under the kitchen table. Seconds later, an enormous fireball crashed onto Caer Fenlli, and a sheet of flame roared into the air. The wooden pallisade walls collapsed burning to the ground and within minutes the entire court had been consumed by fire. An hour later, after the flames had died down, a huge pall of black smoke drifted out over the Vale of Clwyd. Benlli Gawr's palace had been reduced to ashes...

St Garmon stepped outside and clapped his hands together, satisfied at a job well done. He shook Cadell by the hand and gave him his blessing. Then he descended to Iâl to found a church for the inhabitants, divinely freed from Benlli's tyranny. It, or rather its successor, is still there — Llanarmon-yn-Iâl, or *The Church of St Garmon in Iâl*. Cadell did rather well for himself in later years and became King of Powys. And Benlli Gawr lived on.

Despite his size, Benlli the Giant must have been a slippery customer, for he escaped the destruction of his court unscathed. He spent several weeks kicking around the ashes on Moel Fenlli, cursing loudly. He swore that he would kill the next Christian he saw. Unfortunately for him, this was another saint, St Cynhafal. Benlli spotted him making his way up the Bwlch. He leant upon a staff and wore a simple white robe over his shoulders, and a meek but blissful expression upon his ancient face. Benlli recognised him for a Christian at once.

He picked up a boulder and chucked it down the valley. St Cynhafal side-stepped it neatly, and he looked up to where the giant was hopping up and down in a frustrated fury.

"Tut tut, my son," he said "you should learn to control your hot temper, lest it should consume you."

Benlli did not take his advice, and his only answer was to threaten the saint with another boulder. St Cynhafal put his hands together and prayed briefly. Immediately, Benlli's temper ignited within him. Flames burst out of his body, and he dropped his boulder with a scream of terror.

The giant gave a mighty leap off the top of Moel Fenlli and, yelling and shrieking, went hurtling away down the valley. A great arc of oily black smoke followed him as he landed with a tremendous splash into the River Alun. He had hoped that the water would quench the fire raging within him, but the river refused to help, and vanished down a hole underground. The unfortunate Benlli was left thrashing about on a dry river bed.

He picked himself up and desperately threw himself a mile or so further downstream. The water hissed and bubbled, but once again it vanished underground. Benlli gave a final bellow of dismay and then the flames burnt him up altogether. Soon there was nothing left of him but a pile of ashes, dead as those on Moel Fenlli. Every summer, to this day, the River Alun disappears down two swallow holes, leaving behind a stretch of dry river bed.

The Cannibal Giantess

Giants, like Goemagog and Benlli Gawr, could be fierce monsters. So too could the female of the species, and perhaps the most fearsome was the giantess which prowled the boggy wastes to the south of Llandegla. Not only was she as tall as a house, she was also extraordinarily ugly. Worse still, she was a cannibal with a voracious appetite for human flesh. Because the desolate stretch of moorland in which she lived was sparsely populated, she was constantly hungry and this made her terribly bad-tempered. If she did spot some foolish or ignorant soul traversing the moor, she would charge across and snap him up without a moment's notice, dragging him back to some convenient cave to munch on his bones.

Finally, it was decided something positive ought to be done to rid the land of such a nuisance, and a young knight from Glyn Dyfrdwy (the *Dee Valley*) set off to claim some fame for himself by slaughtering the monster. He buckled himself into his best armour, borrowed a good sword and headed north to Cyrn y Brain, the wild country in which she lived.

The young knight spent several hours plodding about the moors in search of the giantess, without success. It had not occurred to him that someone twenty foot tall has a better view of the country than someone only six foot tall, or that the giantess would, in fact, spot him first. Unfortunately, she did. Slowly, she crept up behind him...

Had it not been for the loudness of her tummy rumbling, the young knight would not have known until it was too late, but luckily, he spun around just in time. The giantess' hideous face leered at him greedily, and her warty chin dribbled with saliva.

An awful stench of halitosis wafted from her open maw, and the knight slammed shut his visor at once. Prudently, he raised his sword.

The giantess was fascinated. She'd never tried tinned food before. She reached out one hand for the morsel — and yelped with pain as two of her fingers were hacked off by the knight's sword. She reached out her other hand, and the knight sliced off two more fingers. The giantess regarded her bleeding stumps with astonishment, and then rather foolishly extended both hands. Hack-hack-hack went the knight's sword, and plop-plop-plop went three more of her fingers as they fell amongst the heather.

The giantess wasn't used to such behaviour from a light snack, and she crouched down to get a better look at it. The knight took immediate advantage of this and lunged forward with his sword. He chopped off one of her arms. Finally (for she was rather thick), the giantess decided to fight back. She took up her fallen limb and, using it like a club, began to smack the young knight about the head and body with it. A desperate and bloody battle ensued. It went on for several hours. Eventually, however, the giantess, weak from loss of blood and hunger, staggered, and then fell face down in the heather. The knight climbed onto her back and prepared to behead her.

"King Arthur spare me!" she suddenly screamed, for no apparent reason. The young knight glanced around, in case the legendary king was somewhere on the horizon. He wasn't, so he quickly finished the job.

Deciding that carrying the giantess' ghastly, swollen dead head home in triumph was really too horrible to contemplate, the young knight left the corpse where it lay and stumbled off to find some water with which he might wash the gore from his armour. He shortly found The Well of Saint Collen, bubbling from the hillside, and he lay back in it. The clear waters immediately ran scarlet with blood, and, so it is said, they have ran slightly red ever since.

Idris and Bronwen

High on a peak in the Berwyn Mountains there is a great pile of stones called Cadair Fronwen. Cadair Fronwen means *The Seat of Bronwen*. Bronwen is usually a female name but in this story Bronwen is the name belonging to a large and rather stupid male giant.

This Bronwen had a brother called Idris, who was just as tall and just as dim-witted as he, and who lived many, many miles away in southern Snowdonia. Because they lived so far apart, the giant brothers found it rather difficult to communicate with each other, and so they decided that in order to hold conversations they would each build a tower from which they could stand and shout at each other across the mountain tops. So, they each climbed to the summit of their nearest mountain and began building.

Unfortunately, to help them in their work the giant brothers had between them only one hammer. This they would throw backwards and forwards across the Welsh landscape, each taking it in turns to use it. However, Bronwen was rather selfish and he would call that he wanted the hammer back again almost immediately after he had thrown it. No sooner had the hammer landed at Idris' feet than Bronwen would be calling after it. In this way, Bronwen's building work soon began to outstrip his brother's, and Idris grew jealous.

Finally, he lost his temper. He picked up the hammer, held back his arm and chucked it with all the strength he could muster. It went whistling over Bronwen's head and landed over a mile away at a place called Cwm Llawenog in Llanarmon Dyffryn Ceiriog parish. It landed with such force that it left behind a massive dent, now called Pant-y-cawr, or *The Giant's Hollow*. Because they'd lost their hammer, the two silly giants couldn't continue with their work and both kicked down their towers in fits of pique. All that now remains of their labours are the two heaps of boulders called respectively Cadair Fronwen, in the Berwyn, and Carneddau on Cadair Idris (*Seat of Idris*), in Snowdonia.

Giants in the Earth

In Celtic folklore, stories about giants are most often used to explain certain features in the landscape. Clwyd is no exception to this, in fact the tale of Idris and Bronwen is a good example. There is a similar story concerning some huge rocks which are located in Llanrhaeadr-ym-Mochnant parish, in the very south of the county. They are named Baich y Cawr a'r Gawres and Ffedogaid y Forwyn, or in English, *The Giant and Giantess' Burden* and *The Servant Girl's Apronful*. Like Cadair Fronwen and Cadair Idris, they became part of the landscape due to the building activities of giants.

A giant who lived on a nearby mountain wished to construct a bridge across a depression in the ground called Pant-y-cawr (*The Giant's Hollow*), and he asked his wife and servant girl to help him. He wanted to make it a surprise for his giant friend, who lived on another mountain, and so he determined to carry out the work during the hours of darkness, to have it completed before sunrise. He and the two giant women fetched and carried all night, the servant girl using her apron to carry her load. However, like most giants, they were somewhat dull-witted, and their work was accordingly slow. Cock-crow came upon them unexpectedly long before they were ready. Giving up on the whole idea, the giants threw down their burdens in frustration, and they rest there still.

Further north, at Llannefydd near Denbigh, there are two hollows in the fields Ffridd Uchaf and Ffridd Isaf belonging to Tan-y-Gaer farm. They are called Naid y Cawr a'r Gawres, or *The Leap of the Giant and Giantess*. Two giants once jumped into the fields from their home in the ancient hillfort on Mynydd y Gaer above the village, and the hollows were caused by their impact. The giantess landed in Ffridd Uchaf and the giant in Ffridd Isaf.

On the edge of the Denbigh Moors (*Mynydd Hiraethog*), a quarter of a mile east of the mysterious encampment known as Hen Ddinbych (*Old Denbigh*), there stands an imposing pillar stone, seven foot high and eight foot broad. Lying beside it is a large fragment which has apparently fallen from its apex. It was said that the top of the stone had been sliced off by a giant with his sword, and for this reason it became known by the name of

Maen y Cleddau, meaning *The Stone of the Sword*.

Commonest of all topographical features linked with giants are burial mounds. It seems that our immediate ancestors imagined our distant ancestors as men of enormous physical stature. The heroes of old had taken on quite literally giant proportions. The hundreds of cairns and tumuli dotted around Clwyd were known to be the burial mounds of Ancient Britons, and the continuation of this idea makes it natural that they should have been expected to contain not only the last remains of ancient warriors, but of giants too.

One example is the tumulus situated in a meadow north of Plas Einion farmhouse near Llanfair Dyffryn Clwyd. It was called Bedd y Cawr (*The Giant's Grave*) and was said to be the last resting place of a giant named Einion, who once lived at the Plas.

A cairn at Garnedd House, Llannefydd, was said to contain the remains of a giant who was shot here with an arrow by another Giant. It is possible this story is a memory of an assassination which took place here thousands of years ago. (Perhaps one of the Giants was that responsible for the large hollow at Tan-y-Gaer Farm, described earlier.)

The Bedd y Cawr at Cefn, south-west of St Asaph (*Llanelwy*) is an artificial bank of stones, superficially resembling a grave. It stands on the south-east portion of a limestone ridge called Cefn Meiriadog, named after the Giant local tradition says is buried there. Cawr Meiriadog lived at Plas Newydd, a great 16th Century house a half-a-mile or so away. In this house there was once a massive oak screen, which divided the kitchen from a living room, and on it, about nine foot from the ground was shown a peg where the giant used to hang his hat. Unfortunately, this screen was removed many years ago, but it eventually found a home in the Welsh National Museum at Cardiff.

Another Bedd y Cawr is situated at Bryneglwys, and standing upon it is a long stone. It was believed to mark the grave of a giant soldier who was felled in a battle once fought in the adjoining field. In the 1860's the stone was taken down and used as a gatepost by Edward Roberts, the farmer of nearby Penybedw. However, Roberts found the stone completely useless for the purpose, since he could not make it stand up. It seemed to have a mind of its own, and would always fall over. What's more, the foolish farmer found himself plagued with sleepless nights and horrible nightmares, so he finally decided to return it to its proper place on the tumulus. Another farmer, Edward Morris, planted yew trees on either side of Bedd y Cawr immediately afterwards and built a hedgerow round it. From then on no-one would be tempted to remove the stone again.

Edward Roberts was not the only man to suffer from defiling an ancient burial mound, for these tombs seem to have been protected by curses similar to those alleged to belong to Egyptian Pyramids. Belli Gawr, the son of Benlli Gawr, was killed in battle in the parish of Llanarmon-yn-Iâl and was buried between two standing stones on the mountain above the village. In the 1840's, these standing stones were pulled up by a wicked landowner called Edward ap John ap Llywelyn, and placed on the chimney of a limekiln. The heat made them crumble, so he put them inside and burned them for lime. Ever since he did not prosper, and he died in misery, which served him right.

Giant Phantoms

The ghost of a giant was apparently seen in the 19th Century by a young man near Derwen. It was early on May Day morning and the youth had, with a companion, been touring the neighbourhood performing an ancient Celtic custom called "fixing penglogau". Penglogau were sheep skulls which, on May Eve, jilted young men would fix above the front doors of girls who had rejected them. (Fortunate boys would attach a bouquet of flowers above their loved one's door.) The two young men in this story must have been unpopular types, because they had spent all night fixing the unpleasant sheep skulls.

They were on their way home, walking down the road to Melin-y-Llwyn, when suddenly one of the boys saw descending the hill before them a huge man, a giant. He was carrying over his shoulder a tall pine tree in full foliage. When he began to cross over the bridge, he threw the pine tree into the River Clwyd with an almighty splash.

"What was that!" cried the boy's companion. He had seen nothing, and now there was nothing to be seen by either boy, for the giant had vanished.

Another giant phantom, even more mysterious than the last, was seen by a young farm servant who later became a bailiff of

Ruthin (in the late 19th Century). He had been returning home late from Corwen and had just crossed over the bridge known as Pont y Glyn, which spans a deep wooded chasm between Corwen and Cerrigydrudion, when he espied a lady in full Welsh costume sitting on a pile of stones by the side of the road. He raised his hat politely.

"Noswaith dda," he said, but received no reply. Silently, the woman got to her feet and without looking round began to proceed down the road. Then the man gaped with astonishment, for as she walked away, the "woman" began to swell up. She grew larger and larger and fatter and fatter until her girth completely filled the road. She waddled round the corner, and the startled man hurried after her to see where she went, but, like the phantom described previously, she had vanished.

Sir John Salusbury and the Denbigh Dragon

Sir John Salusbury was a knight, a hero, and a Giant, and he lived near Denbigh (*Dinbych*) many, many centuries ago. For exercise every morning he would pull out forest trees by their roots (perhaps it was his ghost which was seen at Derwen), and he became famous nationally when he killed a lioness with his bare hands at the first British zoo, which was in the Tower of London. He was commonly known by the nickname of Sir John of the Thumbs, because he was blessed at birth with the distinction of having eight fingers and two thumbs on each hand. He was also sometimes known as Old Blue Stocking because of the colour of his hose. Because of his prodigious size and strength, Sir John Salusbury was often called upon by the local people in times of trouble.

The greatest moment of crisis came when a dragon — a great, scaly brute with bat-like wings and rows upon rows of long, pointy teeth — decided to make its home in the district. It immediately began a reign of terror. In its search for food, it would swoop down upon farms and bodily carry off cows, sheep, goats, or at worst unlucky farmers, and take them, ready roasted by its fiery breath, to its lair, which was inside the ruins of an old

Denbigh — The Medieval castle, where Sir John of the Thumbs slew the dragon, stands proud above a town which was once the home of Bella Fawr the witch, and was a haunt of the Devil.

castle. The locals wasted no time in sending a deputation to their resident hero and, bashing on Sir John Salusbury's door, they asked him to sort out the venemous serpent which was keeping them in such dread. Sir John agreed to have a go and took down his massive broadsword from above the fireplace and strapped it to his waist. Thus armed, he stumped off up the hill to the ruined castle.

It was about tea-time, and the peckish dragon, impressed by the size of the meal entering its lair, leapt out at Sir John in the expectation of devouring him. But the giant instantly drew his sword and fought back. Unfortunately, he found that the tough metallic scales of the dragon's hide protected it from even the keenest strokes of his blade, and its frequent blasts of flame were blinding. Soon, the knight had to admit that he was experiencing considerable difficulty.

As the dragon flapped its enormous wings, however, Sir John noticed a bald patch of skin at the base of each, and swiftly recognised them as the serpent's possible Achilles heel. He lunged in under the dragon's snapping jaws and thrust his sword deep into one of these soft spots on its hide. The blade penetrated the skin with ease, straight to the dragon's heart.

Down below, the people heard a hideous shriek erupt from the castle ruins and they let out a cheer of triumph when a few minutes later they caught sight of Sir John descending the hill with the slain dragon's head held aloft for all to see. He paraded the monster's head through the town, and the people started up a chant of "Dim Bych! Dim Bych!", which means *No more Dragon! No more Dragon!* Some say that this is how Dinbych got its name.

The Gwiber

More dangerous even than the Denbigh Dragon was the dragon which haunted Llanrhaeadr-ym-Mochnant parish on the Powys border. No-one knew where it came from, but suddenly it was there — a long, black, winged serpent flapping through the night air in search of prey. No living thing was safe from its slavering jaws, for it was quite indiscriminate in its choice of food. It was equally fond of man and beast, although it perhaps particularly preferred the tender flesh of children. It made its lair in the crevice near the top of Pistyll Rhaeadr waterfall, where water splashing from the rocks would cool it while it digested a heavy meal. Sometimes, the falls, crashing 240 foot into the river below, would be tinted a pale pink, stained with the blood of fresh carcasses. The vile creature was named Y Gwiber, which means *the Viper*, and all the land went in fear of it.

Many attempts by brave young men were made to destroy the evil serpent, but always in vain. It was once fought with very long spears, which kept the warriors at a safe distance from its sharp teeth and fiery breath, but the Gwiber smashed them to splinters and devoured the unfortunate men in seconds. Huge boulders were tumbled down a hill to squash it whilst it fed on some beasts left for it as bait, but with a flick of its tail and several flaps of its mighty wings it escaped. Eventually, a group of weary villagers from Llanrhaeadr decided that where brute force had failed cunning, and perhaps a little magic, might succeed, and they journeyed for several days across the hills to the cottage of a wise old woman known to be learned in the lore of the ancients.

The old woman was tiny and frail, but her eyes glittered with

The dramatic falls of Pistyll Rhaeadr, once a serpent's lair.

an almost superhuman intelligence. She seemed almost to have been expecting the villagers in advance, and guessed the reason behind their visit at once.

"You wish to destroy the Gwiber," she said in a cracked and quavering voice. "There is a way. The serpent has a strange weakness, an unreasoned, violent hatred of the colour red. This can be used to one's advantage and its downfall if one is cunning. Listen to my plan..."

The following morning, the band of villagers returned to Llanrhaeadr filled with wonder, and with hope renewed in their hearts.

They returned to the all-too-common news that the Gwiber had claimed yet more lives during the night, and that it now rested in its lair above the waterfall, gorged to the full with human flesh. A meeting of all the village and the outlying farms was called immediately. The wise woman's plan was explained, and at once set into operation. The blacksmith ran to stoke his forge, the rest of the men made their way to the stone quarry, picks over their shoulders, and the women set to boiling up a cauldron of crimson dye and sewing together every spare yard of linen they could find.

All day the people toiled, until, with scarcely an hour of daylight left to them, their preparations were complete. The men had hewn from the quarry a tall pillar of stone, and this they carried to a field lying a few miles south of their village, where, with much heaving and pulling, it was successfully hauled upright. The blacksmith, hot and sweating from his work at the forge, brought to the pillar several dozen long iron spikes and these were wedged fast into holes which had been chiselled into its surface. The pillar now resembled some huge, petrified cactus. Over it was thrown the great red cloth on which the women had been busy all day, and sticks and dry leaves were piled up around it, to form a pyre.

By now, the sun was setting behind the Cambrian Mountains on the horizon and the chill of night began to settle into the people's bones.

"Quickly, light the fire," commanded the head of the village, "the Gwiber will shortly be awake!"

A man got down on his hands and knees and began to rub together two dry sticks, in order to create a spark. It was long in coming, and the villagers huddled together in groups and glanced

Post y Wiber.

around themselves anxiously. Eventually, the wood began to smoulder and the brushwood at the base of the pillar crackled as it caught light. Just then an unearthly cry rent the air. It came from the direction of the waterfall.

"The Gwiber!" a woman screamed, pointing wildly into the distance, and everyone turned their heads. Silhouetted against the skyline was a long, sinuous body with broad, lazily-flapping wings raising it slowly into the air. It was the Gwiber! With one accord, the villagers turned and fled for their homes, the Gwiber's horrible shrieks echoing in their ears, the fear cold in their hearts that at any moment they might feel those terrible jaws closing upon them.

The Gwiber hovered above the fleeing crowd. Never before had it seen so much prey so easy to snap up, and it prepared itself to strike. Then, a light caught its eye. In the meadow, the kindling around the pillar was now burning furiously and the pillar was illuminated boldly by the flames. Draped as it was in the red cloth, it seemed to resemble the long neck of a dragon, rising out of the fire. Perhaps it was this that made the Gwiber instantly attack it.

It hurled itself upon the pillar stone with a cry of fury, and then of pain as the iron spikes beneath the red cloth pierced its body. Forgetting the terrified people completely, the Gwiber lashed down and attacked the pillar again. But the pillar remained sturdy and once more the spikes cut deep into its flesh. Infuriated beyond reason, the Gwiber threw itself again and again onto the stone. It tore at the red cloth, the apparent cause of its blind rage, and the iron spikes beneath tore into it even more cruelly. Finally, its vile body was gashed horribly all over and it collapsed into the fire, dying from exhaustion and loss of blood. It lay writhing in the flames and then with one last piteous shriek, it died. The land was safe from the Gwiber forever.

Today, the pillar stone which was instrumental in the Gwiber's destruction still stands near the village of Llanrhaeadr-ym-Mochnant. It is called the Post Coch (*Red Pillar*) or Post-y-Wiber (*Pillar of the Serpent*).

Dogs of Darkness

Some of the commonest and also scariest monsters to appear in Celtic folklore are the black dogs, enormous black hounds said to haunt lonely roads at night. They were the size of bullocks and had shaggy coats and flaming red eyes which would burn out of the darkness to mesmerise with fear solitary travellers. Sir Arthur Conan Doyle used the black dog legends as inspiration for his well-known Sherlock Holmes story *The Hound of the Baskervilles*. The apparitions were sometimes said to be death omens. Certain roads in particular were often known to be the routes along which a black dog would walk, and inns which one sees named The Black Dog usually stand at one end of such a road. The black dog is known by different names all over Britain, including Padfoot, Trash and Skriker. In Wales it is called the Gwyllgi, *The Dog of Darkness*.

A Gwyllgi was once seen by the grandmother of the famous folklorist T. Gwynn Jones in the 19th Century. He tells the story in his book *Welsh Folklore and Folk Custom*. His grandmother and grandfather were riding on horseback from Ruthin one evening, when, passing a roadside house, the former's mount suddenly shied and pressed close to the hedge. On the opposite side of the road there suddenly appeared a huge, black mastiff-like hound "with baleful breath and blazing red eyes". T. Gwynn Jones' grandfather, who was riding behind, saw nothing and his steed did not react, as the other horse had done. The Gwyllgi paid them no attention but continued down the road until it vanished from view. The couple were then newcomers to the district and did not learn until later that the house which they had passed had a strong reputation for being haunted.

Elsewhere, but also in the 19th Century, another Gwyllgi was encountered by a man named Edward Jones, one-time sergeant in the Denbighshire Yeomanry. The experience frightened him badly at the time, but he loved to talk about it afterwards. Late one night, riding home across the moor from a fair held at the village of Cynwyd, near Corwen, he suddenly found himself followed by what he called *the Black Hound of Destiny*. He described it as "a beast of fearsome visage and blood-shot eye" and it padded silently behind his horse as if it were preparing at any moment to pounce. Expecting at any moment to feel the

53

hound's hot breath on the back of his neck and its monstrous paws upon his shoulders, poor Edward suffered in some anguish for a considerable time.

Eventually, he summoned up the courage to glance around, and he was extremely relieved to find that the Gwyllgi had ceased stalking him and had disappeared.

Even more dreadful for the lone traveller to encounter were the Cŵn Annwn, or *Hounds of the Underworld*. They were packs of spectral dogs which hunted through the night sky, their eldritch baying freezing the blood of anyone unlucky enough to hear it. It was said that they were once human souls whose evil and ungodly ways had twisted them into demons condemned to roam the earth forever in search of souls as dark as their own, which they would capture and drag back to hell. Sometimes their hunting was directed by the Devil himself, and he would ride behind them on a black charger, cracking a whip above their heads.

Anyone coming across a pack of Cŵn Annwn would hide behind a tree or throw themselves flat upon the ground and hope that their souls were not wicked enough to merit the hounds' attention. Sometimes it was touch and go. They would sniff around their proposed victim, rubbing their sleek, grey, red-spotted pelts up against him and, with their eyes glowing, they would peer through his mortal flesh to examine his soul. Then, if the poor man was fortunate, they would abandon him and chase off in search of a worthier (or perhaps I should say unworthier) quarry. Marie Trevelyan in her book *Folklore and Folk Stories of Wales*, which was published in 1909, says that such a fate befell an Englishman in the Vale of Clwyd. He was "nearly killed by the Cŵn Annwn", and gladly made his escape.

These tales of the Dogs of Darkness end this chapter of Monsters. The darkest monster of all, the Devil, also had his haunts in Clwyd, and some accounts of his exploits are recorded in the next chapter.

Monsters — Bibliography

Helaine Newstead, *Brân the Blessed in Arthurian Romance* (Columbia University Press 1939).

Geoffrey Ashe, *A Guidebook to Arthurian Britain* (Longman Traveller Series).

Michael Senior, *Myths of Britain* (Book Club Associates 1979).

Rev. Elias Owen, *Welsh Folklore* (Oswestry and Wrexham 1896 & EP Publishing Ltd 1976).

Rev. Elias Owen, *Old Stone Crosses of the Vale of Clwyd* (Oswestry and Wrexham 1886).

Rev. Ellis Davies, MA, FSA, *Prehistoric and Roman Remains in Denbighshire* (Cardiff 1929).

W. Jenkyn Thomas, *The Welsh Fairy Book* (Fisher-Unwin 1907 & John Jones Ltd 1979).

T. Gwynn Jones, *Welsh Folklore and Folk Custom* (Author 1930 & T.S. Brewer 1979).

Marie Trevelyan, *Folklore and Folk Stories of Wales* (Eliot Stock 1909).

Ken Radford, *Tales of North Wales* (Skilton and Shaw 1982).

Thomas Pennant, *A Tour in North Wales* (London 1784).

G.J. Howson, *Overton in Days Gone By* (Oswestry 1883).

Byegones.

Chester Chronicle.

THE DEVIL

Recently, the churchyard wall at Meliden, near Prestatyn, needed to be repaired when it was found to be so unstable that it was in danger of collapse. During its restoration it was found that the ground beneath it was crammed with skeletons. It is just possible that the reason why these had been buried there was that their past owners had all been people who had sold their souls to the Devil. There are many tales told in Wales of wicked, rough-living men who, in order to obtain more earthly pleasures, signed over their souls to the Devil. They used a contract which included a clause allowing the Devil to claim the men's spirits, when they died, whether or not their bodies had been buried in consecrated ground. However, before they died the men would leave in their wills the command that they should be buried directly beneath the churchyard wall, and therefore neither in nor outside consecrated ground. In this way, they would cheat the Devil of his prize. It appears, therefore, that Meliden must at one time have been the home of an extraordinary number of unrepentant sinners...

In Clwydian folklore, the character of the Devil is not significantly different to that described in tales from the rest of Wales. His purpose seems to have been mainly comic, like a character in a mummer's play. In fact, he is often made out to be something of a buffoon. Frequently, he is described as taking the form of an elegant, rather effete, black-dressed gentleman, who would roam the countryside and, with the use of considerable amounts of unctuous charm, try to trick people into selling him their souls. A stout-hearted Welshman, however, was normally more than a match for him, and he was usually discovered and routed. His task was not simply to tempt honest men and women, but also to punish the ungodly, in particular persistent

Sabbath-breakers and those who were wicked or foolish enough to try and claim allegiance with him.

The Devil could assume the form of many things, but his undisguised appearance was apparently that of the goat-like Beast found in Medieval sculpture and manuscripts — with horns on his head, great hoofs on his feet, and the possession of a long, pointed tail. Sometimes he was huge. A drover named John, of Ty'n Llidiart near Pentrefoelas in west Denbighshire, was taking some cattle to be wintered in the Vale of Clwyd when he came across the Devil lying right across the road, his hoofs resting on the hedge on one side, his horned head resting on the other. He was moaning horribly and stinking of brimstone. Poor John, not surprisingly, turned on his heel and ran straight home to his wife who, having already smelt the sulphur, was relieved to find that it was only him!

In this monstrous guise, the Devil, in common with other larger-than-life figures such as giants and King Arthur, would sometimes be credited with the creation of prominent landmarks. In Clwyd he was said to have built Wat's Dyke, a linear earthwork which, like its more famous (and, historically, slightly more recent) cousin, Offa's Dyke, was designed as a boundary between Wales and the English principality of Mercia. However, whereas Offa's Dyke stretches all of the 193 kilometres connecting the north and south coasts of Wales, Wat's Dyke terminates near the Shropshire Border. It was said that the Devil had wished to construct a boundary to separate Wales from England, in order to claim the wickedest country as his own (I won't hazard a guess which this was, however!). He had with him an accomplice devil to speed the task, but they were interrupted halfway through. A cockerel was startled awake by the sounds of their labours and crew loudly, thus confusing the devils into thinking that dawn was about to break. Daylight is anathema to the Devil's dark deeds, so with a cry of "We'en stay!" they downed tools and ran off, leaving the work unfinished. Through the course of time, Wat's Dyke has been flattened out of all recognition in many places, and the above story was actually told by the inhabitants of Ruabon (*Rhiwabon*), who believed that it terminated near them.

It was once considered almost blasphemous to refer to the Devil directly, so he goes by a variety of other names in Clwyd. *Diafol* or *Diawl* are the literal Welsh equivalents to Devil. Other

Meliden Church.

Welsh names, such as Cythraul do not have direct translations but mean something like *fiend*. He went under many other epithets, such as Y Gŵr Drwg (*The Bad Man*) or Ysbryd Drwg (*The Wicked Spirit*) or, perhaps more affectionately, Yr Hen Fachgen (*The Old Boy*). In North Wales especially, he also bore the name Andras. Biblical names such as Satan or Beelzebub were acceptable, and also some strictly English ones, such as Old Nick and Old Harry, crept into usage. Most commonly, though, he was called the Evil One, which sums him up quite neatly.

Why The Devil Is Black

Andras the Evil One, many hundreds of years ago, once retired to a large cave near the sea, on Pen-y-cefn Mountain not far from Llanddulas in north Denbighshire. From here, on moonlit nights, he would sally forth to commit deeds of mischief against the poor people living in the surrounding country. His favourite trick was scaring pregnant women. He would select a lady heavy with child, then wait until she was at her most unsuspecting, perhaps getting ready for bed, tidying herself in front of her mirror. Then — boo! — he would leap out from nowhere, a horrible expression leering on his ugly face. The poor woman, on catching sight of his startling reflection, would give out a terrific yell and most probably faint from fear and surprise. Naturally enough, the Llanddulas parishioners soon got rather tired of this sort of behaviour, and so approached the parson on the matter of doing something about it. Full of sympathy, the holy man immediately rallied round a few of his colleagues and, in the company of a specially-sent for expert on such matters, they all set off up Pen-y-cefn Mountain to perform an exorcism.

They soon reached the dark and forbidding cavern that had become the home of the Evil One, and, summoning up their courage, they quickly laid out a bell and a candle and opened their heavy church Bible. As soon as the first lines of the exorcism were read, the Devil, anguished by the holy words, began to roar furiously. Then he sprang out of the cave, reeking of sulphur, and, clapping his hands over his ears, ran off down the hill. He was in such a hurry to escape the priests that halfway down he tripped over an outcrop of rock and fell headfirst into a pool of black mud. And that, so it is said, is the reason why the Devil has been black ever since.

The Uninvited Guest

In a large farmhouse called Henafon, not far from Rhuddlan, a party was being held. All the young men and women from the district were there, singing and dancing and generally getting to know each other. Sometime in to the evening, when the merriment seemed in danger of flagging a little, someone suggested a game of cards to liven things up. The cards were fetched and the young people began to sort themselves out into teams. Just then, a light rapping was heard at the door. The door was opened and in stepped a fine gentleman dressed entirely in black. He was tall and lean and had a pointed black beard. In his hand he carried a silver-topped black cane. He bowed low.

"Good evening, young ladies and gentlemen," he said, "honoured I am to make your acquaintance. It was so cold outside and I wondered whether I might just come inside and — ah, cards!"

And with that, he pressed himself upon the company, who were too polite to gainsay him. He strolled over to a group of farmers' sons sitting at a table, and, bowing low again, asked if he might join them in a game? Since there were only three of them and they needed a fourth to make up a team, they agreed. They fancied themselves as good players, and since they were rather well off compared with most of their friends, they were also rather proud. They felt that they would have no trouble in fleecing this somewhat smarmy stranger, and so teach him a lesson for being so forward.

As it turned out, however, the man in black was an exceedingly good player and won game after game. He was also a rotten sport. Every trick he won, and every shilling he extracted from his young opponents, he gloated over, and each game caused him increased mirth and excitement. Finally, the boys had each just one coin left.

"One more game, and then perhaps we can play for a higher stake," the stranger hinted, winking suggestively. It was his turn to deal, and this obscure comment seemed to excite him so much that he was somewhat over-enthusiastic in his shuffling and a card popped out of the pack. One of the young men bent down to retrieve it from the floor. The he cried out in terror.

"Diafol!" he screamed.

The stranger stumbled back in his chair and the youth pointed wildly at his feet. Everyone looked, and it was only then that the assembled company noticed that the stranger was not wearing boots, but that where his feet should have been there were — hoofs! Everyone drew away, and the Evil One turned purple with rage at being discovered.

"Bah!" he spat, and turned into a great hoop of fire. He disappeared up the chimney in a blazing temper.

A Game at Midnight

Robert Llwyd Harri was the champion card player of his day, and although his only legitimate employment was as a farm servant at Gilar Farm near Pentrefoelas, this sideline served to line his pockets with a good deal of silver. In fact, he devoted all his energies to "the Devil's Picturebook", as they were once known, and was not averse to a little cheating here and there. He played every day of the week, including the Sabbath — which was considered a dreadful sin. One night, returning home after a particularly profitable evening's gambling at Rhydlydan, in an iniquitous den bearing the seemingly innocent name of Aunty Anne's House, he was met at the cross-lane by a dark-suited stranger.

"Good evening to you, sir," greeted Old Nick (for it was, of course, he). "Going my way?"

He stepped in with Robert and together they journeyed down the road a little way. The Evil One soon charmed his way into conversation with the gambler and shortly turned the subject round to card playing.

"Why not have a game with me now, sir?" he suggested. It was late and Robert didn't really fancy the idea.

"I'm afraid I have no cards," he said, as an excuse.

"On the contrary, my dear sir," admonished the Evil One with mock surprise, "you have two packs in your breast pocket."

Robert was so taken aback by the stranger's knowledge that he unconsciously drew out both packs. By this time, they had reached Rhyd-y-Cae Bridge, which spans the River Conwy along the Clwyd-Gwynedd border.

Smiling congenially, the Evil One sat on the parapet of the bridge and patted the space next to him invitingly. Robert sighed. Well, he thought, if the silly old man wants to lose a few coins that was up to him. He swiftly dealt the cards and set to playing. It soon became apparent to the experienced gambler that his opponent was a complete muff. It was as if he had never played at cards before in his life. Hand after hand, coin after coin, Robert won. It was almost too easy.

"Oh dear," sighed the stranger. "I'm beginning to run out of funds. Why not come back to my home, Plas Iolyn, it's not far from here?"

"No thank you," replied Robert firmly. Plas Iolyn, he knew, had been deserted for many years and was virtually a ruin. Why did the stranger wish to go there — did he mean to rob him?

"But I'm getting bored with playing for worthless coins," continued the Evil One. "Why not play for a higher stake? Something I'm sure you won't miss. How about playing for... your soul?"

A chilly breeze wafted down off the hill side and a card was blown over the edge of the bridge. Both players inadvertently looked down over the parapet — and there Robert saw, reflected in the moonlit water, not the head and shoulders of the man sitting next to him, but the head and shoulders of a Horned Beast!

"In the Lord's name...!" he cried out, and then turned to face the stranger. But the stranger had gone, and down the road was wheeling a ring of fire...

Although many people would have taken this encounter as a warning, Robert did not do so, but continued to devote his life to gambling. Finally, his time came. He was returning home from playing cards many years later when, on Maesgwyn Bridge, he spotted a hoop of fire burning in the air above him. He realised that it was the Evil One, and for a moment thought of running back to safety. But he was a confident man, and remembering how he had cheated the Devil before, he took heart. In his pocket he happened to have a Bible (which he probably won in a game) and so he felt he had nothing to fear.

He continued on his way, and the hoop of fire descended upon him and snatched him up. He was whirled into the air, many hundreds of feet above the ground. Trying to regain his courage, he managed to drag the Bible from his pocket and, as he had done once before, he called out:

"In the Lord's name!"

The Devil released him. Robert Llwyd Harri fell to his death into a lake. His broken body was never recovered, and the lake was ever afterwards known as Harry's Lake.

Rev. Baddy and the Devil

The Rev. Thomas Baddy was a dissenting minister, a high-minded, worthy man who lived in Denbigh in the 19th Century. One night, as he was sitting at the desk in his study, working on a sermon he intended to preach to his congregation the following morning, he heard behind him a derisory chuckle. He stopped writing. More chuckles followed. Then the room became full of the unpleasant sound of scornful laughter. The Rev. Baddy decided not to look round. He felt sure it must be no more than Satan, come to mock him over his holy work. Well, any dissenting minister worth his salt is more than a match for such as he, the Rev. Baddy thought. He considered for a moment, and then, taking a scrap of paper, wrote upon it the scripture 1st John, 3rd from the Holy Book:

"For this was the Son of God manifested, that he might destroy the works of the Devil."

He held it behind him. The scoffing laughter ceased at once. And the Devil came no more to annoy the Rev. Baddy.

A Lost Soul

Ffynnon Ddôl was an ancient well sunk in a field near Llanddulas; sunk so deep that it was said to be bottomless, reaching down to the very pit of Hell. Here, one black midnight, an old farmer took three sips of water and spat them out, each with a curse against God. The previous winter, his only child had been in the throes of a long, burning fever, and every moment of every anxious day he had prayed with all his soul that she would recover. But she did not. And the bitterness that lay upon his heart was insoluble. He felt that God had forsaken him. At his daughter's burial, neighbours could hear him muttering blasphemies under his breath, and from that day he was a changed man. He kept himself aloof from other's company, and would roam the hills shaking his fist at the heavens and calling out to the Devil. Finally, he renounced his faith with the ritual described above; the three sips of water represented the Holy Trinity, and each contemptuous spit was his rejection.

The next morning, the farmer, perversely satisfied with himself, went back to the work he had neglected for so many months and took his plough-team to plough Ffynnon Ddôl field. It was a bright, sunny Spring morning and the work went well. Soon he was guiding the plough past the wall surrounding the bottomless well. He smiled to himself, remembering the night before, and then shivered unexpectedly. The day had suddenly become colder. And the sky was darkening. Great banks of black clouds rolled in from the sea and swelled overhead. Here and there large drops of rain began to splash against the earth. The atmosphere grew colder still, and the farmer felt a chill penetrating his flesh, through to his heart. The shire horses wickered nervously. Abruptly, a terrific bolt of lightning flared across the land, and a deafening explosion of thunder boomed down from the sky. The horses panicked and reared up, their silhouettes etched against the skyline. The farmer screamed with terror...

The mysterious storm broke up as rapidly as it had arrived. The thunder clouds melted into the pale blue sky and peace returned. Of the farmer there was no sign. His horses grazed contentedly in one corner of the field and his plough leaned up against the wall of Ffynnon Ddôl well. But he was never seen again.

The Fate of Black-Hearted Ifan

Ifan Calon Ddu (*Black-Hearted Ifan*) was a cruel and violent man, a bully, a thief, some said even a murderer. In his large, decrepit house above a remote village in the Vale of Clwyd he kept the company of rogues and villains. His windows would be ablaze all night and the sound of raucous laughter would echo about the shadowed hills until first light. Many people, it was said, had crossed the threshold of his evil den, never to emerge. It was said also that Black-Hearted Ifan had added grave-robbing to his nefarious activities, and that some time in his infamous past he had sold his soul to Satan. People believed that his end would be a shocking one, and they were not disappointed...

It was All Hallow's Eve, just after sunset, and some children were playing outside their homes, laughing and making each other squeal delightedly with scary tales of witches and goblins. Through the gloom they saw the flickering lights of two lanterns approaching them, and then their cries turned to cries of real fear when they recognised the bulk of Ifan Calon Ddu bearing down on them. They scuttled behind a hedge and peeped out cautiously. Of even more terrifying aspect than Ifan was the companion who strode along beside him. He was every inch as tall, but gaunt, and dressed like an undertaker, all in black. The guttering light of his lantern illuminated an emaciated, death-like face, out of which stared two cold, grey eyes. The two grim figures strode by in silence, and then turned at the church and passed through the cemetery gates.

Daring each other, the children crept closer. They could see the two lanterns wavering among the headstones, and in a moment they heard raised voices. A heated argument was apparently taking place. Then, they heard the sounds of a struggle. Suddenly, a piercing scream sliced through the darkness, and one of the lanterns went out. The children turned and fled.

The story they had to tell was not believed at first. However, after Ifan's house had remained in dark silence for several days, and the evil man himself had not been seen, a search was mounted. A corner of the cemetery was found to be in disarray. A fresh grave had been dug, and an upturned coffin lay by its side. All about the graveside were Ifan's footprints, leading nowhere. The adjacent grass verge had been torn up as if by the hoofs of some animal. Black-Hearted Ifan had been reclaimed by his master.

The Afon Trystion bubbles into a pool above Cynwyd — perhaps the one where the Devil trapped an unlucky angler.

The Devil Fish

In the little village of Cynwyd, south of Corwen, there lived a godless man, a farm servant, who never went to church and had no respect for the Sabbath. In fact, he used to spend all his Sundays fishing. The Evil One determined to get him in his clutches.

One Sunday morning, when all his neighbours were in their best clothes, filing to church, the godless farm servant collected his rod and line and went out fishing as usual. He climbed above Cynwyd until he reached a spot where there were several clear pools of water fed by a beautiful waterfall. He sat himself down on a rock by the side of his favourite pool, which he knew to be full of fish, and attached some bait to his hook. He cast into the water.

Suddenly, he caught sight of an enormous, glistening fish a few feet away, swimming just under the surface. Its big, cold eye seemed to be staring at him almost challengingly. Very slowly, the fisherman drew in his line and prepared to cast again. The great fish swam a few yards further into the pool. The fisherman ventured a little way into the water and reeled out some extra line. Tantalisingly, the fish swam out even further. The angler cursed, but followed until he was up to his waist.

"I will catch this fish," he vowed, "though the Devil take me."

At these words, the fish gave a mighty flick of its powerful tail and darted off through the water at tremendous speed. At first it seemed to be swimming away, but then it came round in a circle. Round and round it swam, spiralling in towards the pool's centre and gaining momentum with every circuit. Soon it could just be seen as a silver blur streaking through the water, creating huge circular ripples in its wake. When it reached the centre, it vanished.

But a great whirlpool had been set in motion, and, crying out in alarm, the farm servant realised he was being dragged under the water. He struggled, but could not escape the current. He screamed and screamed, but inexorably the whirlpool sucked him under. His last scream produced nought but little bubbles of air, which rose to the surface and burst in the middle of the pool. His body was never found.

Bachegraig

Bachegraig was a very mysterious house indeed. It was built at Tremeirchion in Flintshire, in 1567, by Sir Richard Clough, whose wife was the mother of Sir John Salusbury, the slayer of the Denbigh Dragon (see the previous chapter). Officially, it was described as being designed after the Dutch-style, but in fact it was more like an Egyptian pyramid, with six storeys that diminished in width from the ground floor to the apex. This strange edifice was constructed with such astonishing rapidity (some say overnight) that it was popularly believed to have been built by the Devil himself. A nearby stream is still called Nant-y-Cythraul (*The Evil One's Brook*), for it was here that the Old Boy cooled the bricks he had baked in his own infernal pits.

Sir Richard Clough was an astrologer (and therefore a bit of a wizard), and he had an observatory in the form of a tiny, windowless room stuck on the very top of the house. It was the persistent rumour round Tremeirchion that here he spent hours on end in deep conversation with the Evil One, discussing magic and alchemy and other godless subjects. It was also the suspicion in the mind of Sir Richard's wife. She was never allowed near the observatory, which could only be reached up a rickety flight of wooden stairs. However, she finally made up her mind to find out what exactly did go on in that little room. No husband of hers was going to consort with the Devil!

Taking her skirts in her hands, she crept up the stairs, careful not to creak any of the loose boards. When she reached the closed door of the observatory, she thought she could discern the muffled sounds of conversation coming from behind it, so she placed her ear against it and strained to hear. She could make out her husband's voice speaking in a low tone, and also a deep, gruff voice she did not recognise. Quickly, she put her eye to the keyhole. Sir Richard was sitting with his back to her, cross legged, chatting amiably with a large, black-clothed gentleman with horns on his head, hoofs on his feet, and a long, pointed tail sticking out of his breeches. Lady Clough threw open the door. The occupants of the room leapt up in surprise, and the Devil gave a roar. He grabbed Sir Richard round the waist and charged away with him through the wall, scattering bricks and mortar in every direction.

Bachegraig does not stand any more. After this incident, no-one would live there, and it fell into a ruin. However, interestingly enough, before it disappeared forever a man who worked at the Buckley brickworks took away one of the bricks with which it had been built, and analysed its contents. He found that its main component was a lava — a quite unusual lava called phonalite, which is not found anywhere in Wales or England. In fact, its nearest location is in rocks hundreds of miles away in Scotland. Is it possible that the Devil brought his own lava, from the fiery pits of hell, to make his bricks?

The Devil in Cerrigydrudion Church

The little stone church at Cerrigydrudion in south-west Denbighshire was once possessed by the Devil. After nightfall, it would glow as if on fire, even though its interior was always deathly cold. At all times of day sinister noises — cackles, low murmurings and chilling screams — would emanate from its walls. Most disturbing of all, passers-by would catch sight of the Evil One himself, his horrible horned face grimacing from the north window or popping up among the gravestones. Not surprisingly, the church soon became deserted, for no member of the congregation would dare visit it. This pleased the Devil greatly, because in this way he was stopping scripture being read, and the people were becoming more and more ungodly. For some reason, the parson was unable to exorcise the evil squatter. He may have lacked the necessary faith, so allowing the Evil One to take possession in the first place. Whatever the reason, the villagers decided to bring in help of a different kind. They consulted a Wise Man of Cefn Cyfarwydd, who was skilled in the occult and had much knowledge of the Old Ways.

"Well," he said, "if your Holy Man cannot evict your unwanted visitor, we must resort to other means. He must be dragged out forcibly. I know of only one thing — or rather, two things — which might possess the necessary strength for this task, the Ychain Banawg."

The Ychain Banawg were two huge long-horned oxen which grazed a few miles away on a hill called Cefn Bannog (named after them). They were said to be the offspring of a legendary, magical cow called the Fuwch Frech*, and were enormously powerful. They were also untamed. However, using certain charms told them by the Wise Man, a group of men were able to pacify the beasts and they were harnessed to a stout yoke of rowan wood. Meanwhile, another group of men had forged a thick chain of wrought iron which they took to the mystical well at Llanelian, where it was bathed in the holy water, so that it should be able to withstand the Devil's might.

"Now that we have our tools at hand," the Wise Man said, "all we need is to taunt the Diafol out into the open, where he may be

70

Cerrigydrudion Church.

trapped." And he told the assembled villagers his plan...

On the following Sunday night, Cerrigydrudion church was ablaze with the Devil's infernal power, and as usual the terrible screams and moans of the damned echoed across the churchyard. Crouching down behind the churchyard wall were a score of the villagers, carrying in their arms the blessed chain of iron. Behind a nearby house, out of sight, the Ychain Banawg pawed the ground and snorted impatiently. Inside the church, the Evil One was enjoying himself immensely. Once more, or so it seemed to him, the village was deserted, and therefore one more Sabbath had passed by with no sermon being preached to the people. He chuckled to himself and peered out of a small window above the north door.

His jaw dropped and he gaped with amazement. Pottering between the graves, apparently completely unconcerned, was a pretty young girl. She was carrying an armful of flowers, and was placing posies on each of the graves in turn. She was singing a hymn quietly to herself. Of course, she was not nearly as unconcerned as she appeared, in fact she was being extremely courageous. Had not all her friends and family been hiding behind the church wall a few yards behind her, she would not have been there. But of this the Devil was unaware. He was outraged! How dare this paragon of virtue come tripping into his domain like this? It was an insult to his awesomeness. Well, he would teach *her* a lesson!

The Evil One slammed open the north door and stood imperiously in the entrance, breathing sulphur. A gasp of fear rose from behind the churchyard wall. Fortunately, the Devil was so taken up with the impression he was trying to make that he did not hear it. The girl's heart faltered momentarily, but she managed to keep her composure. She treated the Evil One to a brilliant smile and then she threw her flowers at him. Then she ran for it.

The Devil gave a bellow of rage and, trampling the flowers (which had withered in his breath), charged after her. She just managed to reach the other side of the churchyard gate as the Devil's talons were reaching out for her. Suddenly, to the Devil's astonishment, a gang of people jumped up as if from nowhere and threw a chain around his wrists. Before he could react, the chain was wrapped round and round and squeezed tighter. Two men ran behind him with more length of chain and began to throw it round his body. The Devil, recovering from his surprise, smiled smugly at the assembled villagers and made to break the coils binding his wrists. But he found that he could not — the magic water of St Elian's Holy Well had made them impervious to his demonic strength.

For the first time, the Evil One felt a tinge of anxiety. He began to struggle furiously, but by now all the villagers were pulling tightly on the remaining length of chain, and he was held fast. From around the corner were led the enormous Ychain Banawg, and they eyed the Evil One with baleful indifference. Realising that he was well and truly caught, the Devil began to exert all his charm on his captors in an effort to be released. But the villagers ignored him, and linked him up to the oxen's yoke. So, he resorted to dark and terrible threats, promising to wreak dreadful vengeance on all about him. However, the people were firm in their resolve. Slowly, the Ychain Banawg were led away from the church, and the Devil was dragged after. He dug in his hoofs, but it was no use, the powerful animals were more than a match for him.

There began a slow, laborious procession out of Cerrigydrudion. Not once did the Devil cease his struggling, and his terrible curses echoed around the hills. The more he raged, the more bestial he became. He let off horrible smells and blasts of fire and brimstone, so that the men and women had to stand well and clear. But the great oxen were unperturbed and led him on over the Hiraethog Moors at a relentless pace. En route, the marks of the Devil's hoofs were left on many rocks and outcrops, where he had attempted to dig in his feet to gain a purchase, and these can still be seen today. They are particularly prominent on a crag overlooking the Alwen Reservoir, called the Craig-yr-Ychen (*Crag of the Oxen*). At one point on the journey, an entire wood was set on fire by his breath. Eventually, however, the procession reached its destination.

This was a lake, chosen by the Wise Man, lying on the southern edge of the Denbigh Moors. The people stood back, and the Ychain Banawg plodded into the water. They disappeared beneath the surface, and then, with a final roar of rage and frustration, the Devil was dragged under also. A huge cloud of steam erupted from the lake and the water bubbled and heaved. The Evil One's power was quenched. He was never to return, his threats of vengeance were never realised. The Ychain Banawg did not emerge from the lake, and they were not seen again. The lake was named Llyn-dau-ychain (*Lake of the Two Oxen*)* in their honour.

* *See the story entitled "A Fairy Cow" in the Fairies chapter.*

The Devil — Bibliography

Rev. Elias Owen M.A., *Welsh Folklore* (Oswestry & Wrexham 1896 and EP Publishing Ltd 1976).

Ken Radford, *Tales of North Wales* (Skilton and Shaw 1982).

Folklore, Myths and Legends of Britain (Reader's Digest 1973).

A.G. Bradley, *The Romance of Wales* (Methuen 1929).

Francis Jones, *The Holy Wells of Wales* (University of Wales Press 1954).

Henry Roberts, *Illustrated Guide to Corwen and Neighbourhood* (Corwen Eisteddfod Committee 1902).

Records of Local History and Folklore Contributed by Club Members (Ruabon and District Field Club 1934).

WITCHCRAFT AND SORCERY

Two hundred years ago, in Wrexham, a woman named Sarah Poole accused before the Justice one Elizabeth Parry of the murder by witchcraft of her infant child. She had entered Sarah Poole's abode and had cursed her and her baby with the words "The Devil bless him and thee also". Sarah Poole immediately fell ill and her child was dead before nine o'clock the same night. Witnesses were produced to testify that to their certain knowledge Elizabeth Parry was a witch, and that she had been seen performing other acts of witchcraft in the parish. One claimed to have overhead her uttering the words "The Devil bless this work" whilst watching a woman milking a cow. The cow suddenly stumbled and fell on top of the woman, nearly smothering her to death. However, Elizabeth Parry was acquitted, for the Justice refused to accept the existence of such things as witchcraft. She left the parish shortly after.

The apparent common sense of the Justice of the Peace, however, would probably not have been shared by the majority of his fellow Welshmen. Belief in witchcraft in Wales has always been strong. From earliest times, Welshmen have been convinced of the ability of certain members of the community to alter the physical world around them with the use of magic. Most villages possessed at least one wise woman or man, skilled in ancient lore, whom the rest of the community would consult on matters of love, or luck or illness. Such people would use "white magic" to bring about their aims and were referred to as "white witches". Male white witches who were especially powerful were called conjurers.

However, it was the "black witches", who used witchcraft for evil or selfish purposes, who most concerned the average Welsh villager, for they were laws unto themselves and would use the general fear of their dark powers as a means of extortion. Sometimes black witches were solitaries living alone in ramshackle hovels on the edge of habitations, constantly stirring their great black cauldrons and muttering strange incantations under their breath. Sometimes they wandered the countryside begging for food, threatening to curse with some dire ill householders who refused them charity. Black witches were also frequently members of covens, groups of thirteen who would congregate at midnight on some bare hilltop to consort with their master, the Devil. One such meeting place was Moel y Parc on the northern end of the Clwydian Range.

If someone believed that they had been the subject of a witch's curse, they would seek the help of the local *dat-witchiwr*, or "unbinder of spells", a white witch skilled in the art of casting counter-spells, which would return good fortune to the victim. When a butter-churn at Foel Fawr Farm near Derwen would not make butter one morning last century, it was assumed that it had in some way been bewitched, and the farmer asked a well-known unbinder of spells, E. Edwards from Llwynbrain, Gwyddelwern, for help. Reciting a magic spell, Edwards bound a ring of mountain ash wood around the base of the churn. He then invited the dairy maid to return to her butter making, and she found that the butter began to form almost at once. The mountain ash, or rowan, was believed to have been a blessed tree, and was often used in ceremonies to break spells.

For most people, it was thought better to prevent the effects of a curse, rather than to cure them, and if they could afford it they would hire a sorcerer to make them a charm which they could keep in the house to ward off evil. Just such a charm was discovered in 1960, hidden in a large cruck in the main beam of an old house called Tŷ Gwyn, at Fron Isaf near Chirk (*Y Waen*). It was a piece of parchment, folded into the shape of a pentagon, on to which had been scrawled many peculiar heiroglyphs, and a couple of incantations, allusions from the Bible, which read:

"In the Name of God let god arise and scatter these mine Enemies let Them... Be as The Dust before The Wind and The Angel of the Lord scattering Them. Put on the whole Armour of God That we may be able to stand against The wiles of the Devil."

The charm was probably 18th Century in date. A similar one, dating from the early years of the 19th Century, was discovered not many miles away from the Chirk example at Nantyr, Glyn Ceiriog. The earliest conjurer's charm discovered in Wales was five hundred years old.

In our unenlightened past, the natural causes of disease were not understood and an unexpected visitation of sickness was frequently put down to the intervention of a supernatural agent, namely the "evil eye". Some spell-breakers were especially sought out for their healing abilities. One such was John o'r Foty of Llansilin. He had a great reputation as a healer during epidemics of pleuro-pneumonia and foot-and-mouth disease in cattle. Near Cerrigydrudion, there was once a cistfaen or prehistoric burial chamber which was known by the local people as "The Asylum". It bore the more ancient name of Carchar Cynrig Bwth (*The Prison of Open-Mouthed Cynrig*), and, some time in the distant past, it seems to have been used by a healer of madness. Insane people would be placed into it by this Open-mouthed Cynrig, and they were imprisoned there until they came to their senses.

In her book *Welsh Witches and Warlocks* (Gwasg Carreg Gwalch 1986), Jane Pugh describes the fantastic costume worn by one such healer, a sorcerer from Llanrhaeadr-ym-Mochnant. His ceremonial dress consisted of:

"a long black cloak embroidered with zodiac and cabalistic signs... a tall, pointed sheepskin hat with feathers around the crown and brim, and with a sheep's tail hanging down... (and) a whip, its handle made from a small skull and the thong made from a long strip of eel skin or possibly human skin..."

This healer cured the madness by calling out to Satan in a strange, jibbering voice and then turning round his patient three times. In this way, the demons would be banished from his mind. Such bizarre ceremonies, (and the fees required by the sorcerers), were off-putting to many people, but they could always resort to using magic themselves. Many charms and spells have been passed down the generations and were still in use into this century (quite probably into the present day, in fact).

At Llety'r Falwen (*The Snail's Dwelling*), a gorse clad dale on Flint Mountain, near Old Flintshire's county town, snails used to be gathered and rubbed on warts before being impaled on the branches of rowan trees. It was believed that as the snails died, so too would the warts. The wife of a Victorian vicar at Rhosymedre in Wrexham Maelor was surprised to be asked by a parishioner for a silver shilling from the offertory. The parishioner wanted to melt it down to turn it into a ring, which he would wear to cure himself of fits. To preserve oneself from infection, it was the habit to cut oneself with a knife, nail, or scythe and to keep the instrument well-greased and rust free. For as long as the blade remained bright, it would retain a kind of antiseptic property for its owner, or so it was thought.

In the 17th Century, a book, the *Malleus Maleficarum* or "Hammer of Witches", written by two German priests, heralded a mass hysteria directed towards witches across Europe. In Germany the populations of whole villages were burned to death in a purge instigated by the Church and the Government. In England, the witch hunts were not so extreme, but many opportunist sadists, like Matthew Hopkins, self-styled Witchfinder General, succeeded in murdering in the name of God hundreds of suspected witches, mainly lonely old women too ill-educated to recite the Lord's Prayer. Wales, on the other hand, was remarkably free of such persecutions, and very few cases came to court. When they did, they were usually thrown out by the commendably level headed Justices, as in the case between Sarah Poole and Elizabeth Parry, described above. It is possible that the Welsh, quite used to the presence of witches, black and white, in their communities, did not usually feel it necessary to involve the Law Courts in punishing their miscreants. They had their own methods.

Before I continue with the folk tales of witchcraft and magic from Clwyd, I begin by recounting two witch trials which did take place in the county. These were the trials of the suspected witches of Penley and Llanasa, both described in *Witchcraft in 17th Century Flintshire* by J. Gwynn Williams MA, from the Flintshire Historical Society Transactions.

The Penley Witch Trial

In 1657, Anne Ellis, a widow of Penley in the Maelor Saesneg of Flintshire, was brought to trial for:

"not havinge the feare of God before her eyes but by the instigation of the Divell... did use, practise and exercise certayne wicked and divillish acts called witchcrafts, inchantments, charmes and sorceries..."

Anne Ellis was being accused of four acts of witchcraft against the people of Penley, but during the course of the trial, many examples of her alleged ability to cause harm by magic to those who offended her were recounted by witnesses. She was quoted as having once said that she "could goe... and put any desease uppon anyone". She was held in great awe by her neighbours, and any misfortune which befell them was automatically blamed upon her. If somebody fell ill, Anne was fetched and, rather than being punished or threatened, she was courteously asked to lift the curse placed upon the person concerned and was then paid for her trouble.

Once, the old widow returned to her home to discover that in her absence a little girl named Margaret Hughes had stolen in and eaten her bread. The girl's mother, on discovering what had happened, begged Anne not to put a curse upon her, but she did not reply, just muttered to herself under her breath. That evening, little Margaret fell very ill indeed, and the next day a lump the size of a chicken egg was found swelling beneath her arm. Anne was summoned, and she entered the child's bedchamber.

"How doest thou?" she asked. "Very sick," replied the girl. Anne placed her hand on Margaret's forehead and said:

"God bless thee, thou shalt mend after this," and the next morning the girl was well.

On another occasion, the child of a neighbour who had refused her meat fell sick. She shrieked horribly and ate nothing for four days, until Anne agreed to bless her, after which she recovered quickly. Another child became affected with a swelling in her head and she writhed in agony for a quarter of an hour, screaming and crying out to her father:

"Daddy, the cat was upon my back and has made me bleed!"

Anne was fetched, and she blessed the child several times, and would have touched her, but the girl turned away.

The witch was always handed gifts for her work by the grateful parents, and so, by continually unbinding her own spells, she did rather well for herself. However, she did not always agree to bless her victims. She was once heard to curse a boy named Richard Hughes with the wish that he would become lame. Six months later, while playing with his ball, the boy gave it a particularly powerful kick, and then cried out and fell over. His leg gave him great pain, and he was never able to lean on it again. When asked at her trial why she had done this, she replied with the question, why did he piss down my chimney?

The incident which finally brought Anne to trial involved another young child who fell ill, the daughter of a woman named Elizabeth Jeffrys. She collapsed with a terrible swelling all over her body, and Anne, assumed to be the cause, was asked to bless the victim. She did so, and the child recovered. Unfortunately, it proved to be a brief respite, and the child was soon worse than before. Her relapse coincided with an angry exchange which took place between her mother and the old widow. The poor child told her mother that "it was allwayes soe" when she fell out with Anne Ellis. Anne would not be prevailed upon to bless the child a second time, and on the Whitsunday she died. Distraught, Elizabeth Jeffrys went the rounds of her neighbours, urging them to take some form of action against the witch. Another woman in the village had recently suffered the tragedy of an infant death, and she too blamed this upon Anne Ellis, as did a farmer whose best milk cow had died under mysterious circumstances.

When Anne was brought before the court, she was accused of bringing about by witchcraft the death of the daughter of Elizabeth Jeffrys, the lameness of Richard Hughes and the deaths of the infant and the farmer's cow. Whilst being held for trial, she cunningly slipped past her captors and escaped. She was later recaptured, but was fully acquitted. She presumably continued the rest of her days extorting money out of the superstitious and frightened people of Penley.

The Accusing of Dorothy Griffith

One dark night, in the late 16th Century, one William Griffith, a sailor, stumbled into an alehouse in Llanasa, north Flintshire, with his hair awry and his face as pale as death. He waved his arms about and tried to speak, but no words came out. He looked "affrighted", to quote the subsequent records, and he stumbled into a dark room and hid his face. The landlord's wife, much confused, followed him in and lit a candle. The sudden glare made William Griffith cry out with fear, and he fainted. He was soon brought round, and, through bouts of fainting, he told his story.

The old sailor had been wending his way across the heath,

The Red Lion Inn, Llanasa, scene of the accusing at Dorothy Griffith.

returning to his ship, when he was terrified by the apparition of a glowing woman, who stepped out onto the track, facing him. He recognised her at once as a Dorothy Griffith (apparently no relation), and she had, so he said, "many lanterns lighted about her". William became rooted to the spot with fear as Dorothy Griffith approached him. Suddenly, she vanished, but the lights that had surrounded her continued to hover in the air. They floated away down the track, and William found himself following them. They led him to the alehouse where he now lay.

After he had told his story, William begged that Dorothy Griffith be sent for, so that she could bless him and lift any curse she may have put upon him. Dorothy was duly brought to the inn. At the sight of her, William began to wail and accuse her of being a witch. Dorothy protested her innocence, but felt it just as well to bless the man. Immediately, William announced that he felt well again, and he said that this proved that Dorothy was indeed a witch. He insisted that she be locked up. Poor Dorothy was frog-marched to the nearest gaol, where she was charged with felony.

The people of Llanasa were shocked when the following morning they heard of Dorothy Griffith's arrest. Dorothy made a complaint to the Justice, and he shortly received in addition a petition signed by thirty-one of her neighbours, testifying to her good character. It transpired that William Griffith had long held a hostile attitude towards Dorothy, and this was probably just a continuation of it. The Justice of the Peace was also probably not terribly impressed by the fact that the witness had recounted his story, and made his accusation, whilst languishing in an alehouse. Dorothy Griffith was bailed the next day, and there are no records to suggest that she was ever re-charged.

The Red Curse

One fine morning, a farm wife was busy dunking some wool into a vat of blue dye outside the front door of her farm in Clocaenog parish, when she looked up from her work to see a strange old woman staring at her. The old woman begged for some of the wool and some of the dye. The farm wife really didn't have any to spare, and, frankly, she couldn't believe the old woman's cheek. She politely refused. The old woman glared at her, and then went off muttering. The farm wife shook her head, and continued with her dyeing. She churned the wool around inside the blue dye for a little while, and then drew it out. It came out red!

She splashed the garment straight back into the dye. She dunked it in and out over and over again, but although the dye was plainly as blue as the sky, the garment stubbornly remained bright red. She took it round to a neighbour's house. Her friend asked her whether she had noticed any strangers in the area recently. The farm wife told her about the old woman. They both concluded that she must have been a witch and she had put a spell on her. The farm wife's neighbour offered to do the dyeing for her. She put the red wool into the vat of blue dye and, to the farm wife's great relief, it this time came out the same colour.

Pedws Ffoulk

Pedws Ffoulk was a wicked old witch. She was extremely bad-tempered, cursing whoever crossed her with dire misfortune. Everyone from her home village of Henllan, near Denbigh, would avoid her, because she would take offence even

Clocaenog.

when none was intended. They would keep their faces turned towards the ground if they happened to pass her, for the gaze of her luminous, green, cat-like eyes was believed to bring bad luck to any living thing it fell upon. Not surprisingly, most people were careful to be as polite as possible to her, especially when she came begging at their door.

However, some of her neighbours occasionally got tired of her constant demands for favours, and risked her punishment. One of these was her closest neighbour, a farmer. The farmer and his servants had just finished digging up a crop of new potatoes one afternoon when the hunched, tatty form of Pedws Ffoulk entered the farmyard. The farmhands all crossed themselves and whispered private prayers to themselves under their breath.

"What a good crop of spuds," remarked Pedws. "Give me them!"

The farmhands all groaned. The farmer took a deep breath, and made a decision. This time he would not give in to Pedws. He would *not* give over his potatoes — they were his livelihood. He wondered how he could best put it to the old witch. He said:

"No."

The farmhands groaned louder. Pedws Ffoulk stared at the farmer in amazement. Was he jesting?

The Llindir Inn, Henllan. The village was once the home of the witch Peddws Ffoulk, and at the Llindir Dic Spot the Conjurer cursed the landlord and his wife for over-charging their customers.

"Give me your potatoes!" she demanded.

"No," repeated the farmer, thinking the direct approach was the best. Pedws Ffoulk's green eyes flashed with rage. She gurgled something unintelligible in the back of her throat, and dribble ran down her warty chin. Then she stomped off across the farmyard, splattering mud as she went. The farmhands crossed themselves again, and the farmer breathed a sigh of relief.

Later on that day, the farmer was with his labourers in the field, hitching up a root-picker to a handsome carthorse, his prize possession, when un-noticed by any of them, Pedws Ffoulk passed by in the adjoining lane. She smiled a toothless smile. She knew the proud expression on the farmer's face would soon be one of dismay. She continued on her way. A moment later, the huge carthorse suddenly collapsed. It fell over onto its side and began to whicker in pain. Froth started from its mouth. The men could not understand what was happening and they desperately tried to rouse the animal. However, it was obvious that it was dying. Pedws, unable to resist a glimpse of her handiwork, tripped nonchantly back down the lane. She was spotted by the farmer, and there was no mistaking the evil glee written on her wrinkled face.

"The old witch!" he cried. "She's put a curse on the horse. After her!"

He snatched up a stout rod of iron, which he used in constructing fences, and one or two of his servants followed suit. Another of the servants had, after the morning's adventure, cut for himself a staff of rowan wood and he brandished this threateningly. Both iron and rowan have the quality of warding off the evil power of witchcraft, and so, when the men began to bear down upon her, Pedws picked up her skirts and began to make a run for it. But the farmer soon caught up with her, and she felt his strong hand on her collar.

"In the name of God, you're coming with us," he told her, and he pressed the bar of iron against her throat. The farmhands, inspired by the farmer's courage, and the suffering of the poor horse, helped him to drag her into the field. The carthorse was thrashing weakly on the ground.

"Bless this animal," ordered the farmer. Pedws muttered something surlily, but the animal did not recover.

"Do it properly!" the farmer stormed, and shook Pedws violently.

"God be with this horse," she snapped. The horse stopped thrashing and began to rise to its feet. Pedws wriggled free and ran off, squawling like an angry cat.

One other villager who once defied Pedws Ffoulk was old Sion, the shoemaker. She once asked him to mend her clogs without payment and he flatly refused. That evening, after he had completed his rounds, returning mended shoes to his customers, he collapsed into his best armchair feeling extraordinarily tired. He rested for a little while, and then decided to get up. He couldn't! However hard he tried, he could not rise from his armchair. He called for his wife, but she could not pull him from the chair. She fetched their neighbours, but even their combined strength was to no avail. Sion remembered the argument he had had with Pedws and could only come to the conclusion that a spell had been put upon him.

Bravely, his neighbours decided to confront the witch. They armed themselves with rowan branches and they borrowed a bag of blessed salt (once considered useful in exorcising evil spirits) from the parson. They barged into Pedws Ffoulk's hovel. A huge black cat with eyes identical in colour to the witch's greeted them with a snarl. Pedws herself stood stirring her cauldron. She was not given time to ask what they wanted. She was quickly surrounded, and the bravest young man threatened to pour the blessed salt over her head unless she accompanied them to Sion's house. She eyed them impassively, but she knew rather better than them the effect the salt would have upon her if they carried out their threat. She brushed past them and led the way to the shoemaker's.

She laughed cruelly at the sight of the poor old man stranded in his armchair, but broke the spell by touching his knees, so that they unbent. Sion climbed stiffly to his feet. Pedws waved a scrawny finger under his nose.

"I let you off this time, old fool," she spat, "but do not cross me again. Next time I ask you to mend my clogs for free — do it!" Pedws hissed loudly at the assembled villagers behind her, then spiralled round and round in the middle of the room, and shot up the chimney. Every day from then on, Pedws Ffoulk would call on old Sion the shoemaker to humiliate him into mending her clogs, free of charge, whilst they were still upon her grubby feet.

Caerwys, Witch Town

On the road into Caerwys from the Vale of Clwyd a huge hare leapt into the path of a mother and her young son on their way to market. It glared at them with its glittering eyes for a few moments and then lolloped away. The boy looked up to his mother, who was shaking her head resignedly and patting the neck of the cow they were hoping to sell at the market.

"Oh well," she sighed, "we might just as well go home. Now that old witch has crossed our path, we'll have no luck today."

It was the woman's belief that the hare had in fact been a witch in disguise. At market, they were unable to sell their cow, and went home as poor as they had started out.

This belief in witches being able to transform themselves into hares is very old. The scholar-monk Gerald of Wales reported such stories in his *Journeys Through Ireland*, which was written in 1185, and he refers to them then as going back to "old times". Also going back to old times is the little Flintshire town of

Caerwys, one time "witch town".

Caerwys (arguably the smallest town in Britain). Some say that the 'caer' in its name refers to a Roman fort, but others believe that as a settlement it predates the Romans, and that the whole word *caerwys* is a very old Welsh word meaning "beautiful". Its town charter was granted in 1290 and it was one of Edward I's "new" towns, created at the same time as he was building his castles in Wales (Chirk, Flint and Caernarfon, for example). It still bears the grid-iron plan of streets with which it was developed at this time.

A couple of miles to the north of Caerwys there is located in a field a pile of boulders, in the centre of which stands an upright slab containing several drilled holes. When the Rev. Ellis Davies was researching his book *The Prehistoric and Roman Remains of Flintshire* he was told by the farmer who owned the field that it was once used to burn witches. They were strapped to the upright pillar and dry wood was piled up over the boulders and ignited. The hare witch encountered by the woman and her son on the road into the town would have been but one witch reputed to have lived at Caerwys. Local tales suggest that it was once a haven for practisers of the black arts. Witches still lived at the nearby village of Ysgeifiog in the 1930's, and I know personally

Enclosed by a hedge, the Caerwys witch stake now leans at an angle.

one white witch living even closer to the town, at Afonwen. In the 18th Century, however, Caerwys was the home of a particularly evil witch...

After sundown, when work could no longer be carried out in the fields, the people of Caerwys would retire to their cottages and quickly settle down to slumber. The little huddle of homes around the central square would soon be silent, undisturbed till cockcrow. One black midnight, however, the silence was broken. Through the still air came the cry of a child.

The thin wail of fear was joined by another. Another child cried in the night, and then another and another. Soon there was a chorus of fear, as from all over the town children called out for their mothers. At one and the same time, appalling nightmares had descended on the young ones of the town, startling them awake, and filling them with terror. In their separate homes, their parents tried to comfort them: told them they had had nothing but a bad dream. But they would not be consoled and they would not close their eyes again. They were afraid of the demons they had seen in their rooms, afraid of feeling again the fingers that had been clawing at their tongues...

It was the same the following night. After the last chime of midnight had ceased its echo, all the children screamed out as the nightmares returned. The nightmares returned again the next night, and the next. The children would not rest. Soon, they began to suffer from their lack of sleep. Fear of what the evening's dark would bring made them listless, and they would not eat. They began to waste away. Their parents, worried to distraction by this strange curse that had fallen upon their children, found it impossible to concentrate on their labours. The plough stood idle in the field, the seed remained unsowed. Night after night, the nightmares came to plague their children, and they were unable to discover the cause. The words of the pastor had no effect, and their prayers went unanswered. Then someone mentioned the name of the witch.

The Witch of Caerwys lived in a ramshackle hut on the edge of the town. She was shunned by the rest of the community, and kept herself to herself. If she made her way into the town, the people would spit in her path, and the children would be hurried from her sight. The parents warned their children to stay away from her, but they did not. It was the children's favourite game to taunt the witch. Unbeknownst to their parents, they would go in gangs to her hovel and shout obscenities through her door. As she wandered the countryside in search of food and herbs for her spells, she would be followed and spat at and jeered at, and the laughing children would run away as soon as she rounded on them. They thought that she was just a lonely, smelly old woman. They did not really believe that she could harm them. They had now been proven wrong.

When the villagers first came to question her, she pretended not to be in. They hammered at her door and shouted for her, but she hid in the dark and smiled to herself. Every day they came looking for her, becoming more and more certain that she was the cause of their despair, but she always hid from them. Then, one morning, a child collapsed. Lack of sleep, lack of food and the unbearable strain had finally taken their toll. She was close to death. The people of Caerwys could take no more. Hatred for the witch was absolute.

"Kill her!" demanded the child's mother. "Her curse cannot affect us if she is in her grave!"

In a band, the townsfolk marched to the witch's hovel. They

caught sight of her scurrying behind her door. They formed a circle around the hut and shouted for her to come out, but she hid under her table and would not reply. They kicked at the door and the walls, but the hut was surprisingly sturdy and they could not gain entrance. One man strode into the copse growing behind the witch's home, and came out with his arms laden with dry twigs. He laid them at the hovel's door. At once, the townspeople realised his intention, and as one they entered the copse and gathered as much firewood as they could. They piled it up around the hut. Within, the witch trembled with fear. The pale, drawn faces of the children were expressionless as they watched a man whittling together two twigs to create a spark.

Suddenly, a thin plume of smoke rose from the twigs. There was a crackle, and flames began to lick around the wood. The dry timber ignited immediately, and the hut was quickly ablaze. The townsfolk backed away, but the children, in a group, continued to watch. The dancing flames were reflected in their eyes. From the burning hovel came a high, thin wail, like the cry of a child. In unison, the children of Caerwys smiled. Together they looked forward to a night of untroubled sleep.

The Stag Witch

There was once a lowly hovel, just like that of the Caerwys Witch, standing in the shadow of the splendour of Chirk Castle. In it there also lived a lonely old lady — a lonely old lady who was a black-hearted witch! It was said that she originally came from the Devil's Peak in Derbyshire and that one day officers of King James himself came to apprehend her for her witchery, but, when they tried to sieze her, they found that they had siezed themselves instead, and she had vanished! She re-appeared on the same day, offering to pay a half-year's rent in advance for the hut at Chirk.

The hut was situated in the heart of the Castle's parkland, the ranger of which was a handsome young man named Owen. Owen did not approve of the presence of the old witch in the land under his care, but he was bound to tolerate her. He would pass by her home every evening on his way to visit his fiance, a pretty lass named Mary Fuller, who lived on the edge of the park. The witch was always there, standing in her doorway, stirring her evil-smelling cauldron. Owen would always avoid her gaze.

The night before the wedding — and Owen and Mary held each other close as they whispered excitedly of their hopes for their life together. It was their custom to meet in the forest, spend a few hours in each other's company, and then Owen would escort the girl back to her home. They did not see any reason why they should change their habits on this night. The evening was growing chilly, and Owen held his fiance close as he walked her back to her cottage. He held her tighter when they approached the witch's shack. Mary was frightened of the witch, and would never look at her, for fear of the evil eye. But this evening, she heard her loved one gasp with shock, and she glanced up.

Outside the old woman's home there stood the most magnificent stag. It was a proud and beautiful animal, standing taller than Owen and bearing six points on each of its great antlers. But it was not the sight of the stag that had shocked Owen, but the fact that the old woman was with it, stroking its neck and whispering into its ear as it nuzzled her face. The ranger was outraged! As keeper of the park, it was his duty to protect the deer of the forest, and he was proud of the herd. It made him sick to see the evil hag caressing this magnificent animal so. He unslung the crossbow which hung over his shoulder and he waved it threateningly at the old woman.

"Leave that beast alone! It is the king's property..." and he ran forward, yelling. The stag reared up in panic and bounded into the woods, while the witch, glaring hatefully and fearfully at Owen, hurried behind her closed door.

Owen rejoined his betrothed, who was trembling with fright.

"Oh, Owen," she whispered, "you should not have angered the old woman, not tonight of all nights. What if she were to curse our wedding?"

But Owen put his arm around her even tighter and told her to put all fears from her head: the morrow was to be the happiest day of their lives, and nothing would spoil it. At her parents' door, he kissed Mary farewell and made his way home, his heart as light as thistledown. However, passing the hovel of the old witch, he began to fall into a cold sweat and a nameless trepidation came upon him. The feeling grew as he entered a dark lane which led him to his lodge. Suddenly, he was startled by an unearthly cry — the mewing of some enormous cat. On the stump of an ancient alder tree blasted by lighting was a dark shape. It had eyes like fire and they glared at him malevolently. Owen took a step forward — and the creature spat at him! A quantity of saliva hit him in the face, and it burned his skin agonisingly. Owen screamed in pain, and, cold terror gripping his heart, he ran away, blindly, tripping and stumbling, until he reached his home. There, he dowsed his head in a tub of water to wash the filthy rheum from his eyes, and he fell into a dead faint.

The following morning, Owen put on his finest clothes and tried to shake the memory of the previous night's encounter from his thoughts: for today was the day of his wedding. At the church, the guests were already assembled and his bride awaited him. She was habited in a snow white dress, and in her braided hair white heath flowers were bound. Owen thought that he had never seen Mary looking more lovely. And Mary, taking sideways glimpses at her new husband during the ceremony, felt that she had never seen Owen looking prouder or more handsome. However, in the midst of their joy, there lay upon both their hearts a strange misgiving. The image of the red-eyed creature in the dark lane was engraved on Owen's mind, and Mary could not forget the look of hatred in the witch's face when Owen had threatened her.

After the ceremony, the newly-married couple danced together on the green, applauded by their young friends. Soon it was time for them to retire to Owen's cottage. Laughing, Mary ran off, closely pursued by her husband, and followed by the cheering guests. She did not notice when she passed the old woman's cottage, but Owen faltered in his steps. Then, from out of the hedge burst the stag! It reared up before them, huge and powerful, the six points on its massive antlers gleaming in the sunlight. Mary screamed, and the stag lowered its head and charged.

The poor girl fled for her life, her wedding gown ripping and soiling as she ran through the thicket, and across the green field behind it, to escape the animal. The thicket's twigs and branches caught in the stag's antlers and slowed it down, but also increased its fury. Owen chased after his bride, and the wedding guests tried their best to keep the stag at bay. Halfway across the park, Mary tripped in her once beautiful long gown, and she fell. At that moment, the huge stag burst from the thicket. It bore down upon the unfortunate girl, but her new husband was by now at her side. Just as the beast was lowering its head to run Mary through, Owen took off his coat and threw it over its eyes, sending it into confusion.

"Run, Mary, run!" he cried. Mary turned on her heel and ran to her home for help. The stag flung off Owen's coat and it turned its attention to him.

The ranger leapt upon its back, and the animal bucked and reared. It smashed its flank into the side of an oak tree, and fractured Owen's leg. He tried to retain his seat, but eventually fell heavily to the ground. His arm, too, was now broken. The stag wheeled about, its mouth frothing. It charged forward, and with its terrible antlers pierced the helpless Owen's body through to the heart. He died instantly. Bellowing in triumph, the stag scattered the distraught wedding party and ran away into the forest.

Mary was driven almost mad by the tragedy. In her distraction at the news of her husband's death, she mentioned the old witch. Several of her friends went to the witch's cottage and kicked down her door. There they found the old woman lying stretched out on the floor, dead. It was believed that she had transferred her soul into the body of the stag, in order to exact her terrible revenge. Owen's mangled body was placed in a humble grave in a peaceful corner of his beloved park. Mary soon joined him, for she died from her grief a few months later. Together, side by side, they slumber.

Gwen Goch

Gwen Goch lived with a pack of goblins in a fog-bound cave in the craggy ramparts of an ancient hillfort called Moel Hiraddug. She was scarcely human, but was more goblin herself. Y Brenin Llwyd (*The Grey King*), the spirit of the mists, would frequently haunt the valleys below the Moel, and would blanket the nearby towns and villages with his breath. On such days, Gwen would leave her cave and descend to create havoc among the people. The town of Rhuddlan was her favourite stamping ground, and here, in a variety of animal disguises — hares, greyhounds, or, most incongruously, little lambs — she would terrify children, frighten cattle and cause untold mischief.

Now, this all took place during the time when the overlord of Rhuddlan was Dafydd Ddu Hiraddug. Dafydd Ddu Hiraddug was not a man to be trifled with, and when Gwen Goch's tricks began to cause his town serious harm, he immediately girt on his sword, and went to sort her out.

The Grey King was sleeping on the Moel when Dafydd climbed its rocky slopes, and the fog was so thick that he could hardly see his hand in front of his face. But he did not abandon his mission. He wandered around the summit leisurely, until he heard the weird gibbering of the goblins in their cave, and he knew that he had found Gwen's home. He strode boldly into the cave, and unsheathed his sword. The light from its silver blade was like a burst of sunshine. The goblins, squealing with terror, rushed out of the cave, and ran away forever. Gwen Goch was left cowering against the wall. Dafydd placed the keen point of his sword under the witch's chin.

"You must promise me that you will never, never, come down into the valley and cause my subjects harm again," he commanded. Gwen transformed herself into a baa lamb and bleated pathetically, to put him off his guard. She tried to curse the knight, but her evil power had no effect on him.

"Promise!" yelled Dafydd. Gwen turned herself back into her own ugly shape.

"I promise," she said.

Bella Fawr

So far, all these tales of witches have been concerned only with the black variety. But white witches were as common, and much of the work they were asked to do was the breaking of spells cast by their darker cousins. There was a famous white witch once living in Denbigh named Bella Fawr (*Big Bella*). It is probably she who features in the following, rather sad, story.

One early morning, Bella was stoking up the embers of last night's fire, to give herself a little warmth while the sun was doing its work of evaporating the chilly mists, when she heard a timid knocking at her cottage door. On the doorstep stood a pretty young girl, shivering in the cold. Under her arm she carried a black cockerel, which was the acknowledged tribute paid to a white witch from whom one wanted help. This she gave to Bella.

"Oh, mother, can you help us?" she asked.

"Come in, child, come in, and tell me of your trouble. I shall do my best." Bella assured her. The girl sat on a wooden stool by the fire and told the old woman that she came from a farm near the village of Bodfari. The night before last, she said, all the animals on the farm had suddenly become affected by a terrible malady. They collapsed, their legs twitching, and could not be made to stand. They would not feed, but lay in a swoon, slowly dying. The girl started to cry. If the animals did die, she said, it would mean the end of the farm and starvation for the family. It was their belief that some jealous soul had bewitched the farm.

"Ah, I fear you are right, my dear," said Bella. She had become experienced with the unbinding of many similar curses, and the remedy she had ready-made into a potion. This took the form of a cunning mixture of herbs, and she passed a small bag of the blend to the farm girl, with this advice:

"At nightfall, take a hair from the back of every beast on your farm affected by the curse, and throw them together on the fire, along with these herbs. Your animals will immediately recover. Now, be along with you," she said, "for I have much else to see to."

The girl hurried home to her joyful parents, and at sunset they carried out the witch's instructions. They plucked hairs from the backs of every animal on the farm and threw them on the fire with the herbs Bella had given them. And at once, the animals got to their feet and shook off their fever.

All, that is, except one. In their excitement, the family had overlooked their old, faithful hound, lying feebly in its corner of the kitchen. And that is why this story does not have an altogether happy ending. For, while all the other animals on the farm recovered from the spell, the poor, sad dog passed away neglected.

Dic Spot the Conjuror

Dic Spot the Conjuror lived in the 18th Century. He was so named because he had a large black spot — a birthmark —

situated prominently beneath his nose. His real name was Richard Morris, and he was very famous. The newspapers were full of the reports of his death in 1793, for, as he lay on his deathbed, the wainscot behind his head rapped mysteriously and unceasingly and the sorcerer predicted exactly the moment of his passing. He told the well-wishers gathered round him that he would die when the light in his room faded. Not long after, the oil in the lantern ran out, and the light it cast flickered and dimmed. And at that moment, Dic Spot was found to have expired.

The best known story told about Dic's antics centres around an inn at the small village of Henllan, near Denbigh (probably the ancient, thatched Llindir Inn). Dic had been making his way to Llanrwst, and stopped at the inn for a meal. His were simple needs, and he asked for nothing fancier than a mug of ale, a loaf and a hunk of good cheese, which, when provided, he enjoyed greatly. He did not, however, enjoy the bill. The landlord charged him an astronomical 4d for the beer and a shocking 6d for the bread and cheese. In the 18th Century, this was daylight robbery!

Dic Spot was outraged, and decided to teach the greedy publican a lesson. He wrote out a spell on a corner of the bill, and then he stuck it under the table's leg. He scattered a few coins on the bar, and left. The landlord and his wife, who had already been preparing for bed, heard the front door bang shut, and they sent their fat serving maid downstairs to make sure their customer had paid. They settled down to sleep, but were startled by the sound of dancing coming from the bar. A loud braying voice floated up to them, singing:

"Six and four are ten,
Count it over again!"

The landlord immediately got up, and went downstairs to find out what on earth was going on. He opened the door to the bar, and there found his maid capering around the floor like a mad thing, and singing over and over again this apparently meaningless verse. He stamped into the bar, to give her a piece of his mind, but the moment his foot touched the floor, he too began to dance, and he began to sing:

"Six and four are ten,
Count it over again!"

Her husband not returning, it was next the turn of the landlord's wife to come down to find out what was happening.

There she was met with the scandalous sight of her husband dancing around the public bar with their serving maid! In a fury, she snatched up a heavy stick to strike them with, and strode into the bar. Of course, her foot touched the floor, and — well, I'm sure you've guessed.

The row the dancing three were now making soon attracted the attention of their neighbours, who one at a time came to investigate. They too found themselves unwittingly joining in with the enchanted dance. As more and more curious people turned up, the bar became crammed with madly, and sadly, dancing folk. Fortunately, at last, one villager rather more intelligent than his neighbours came upon the scene, and guessed at once that here was sorcery at work. Through all the singing of:

"Six and four are ten,
    Count it over again!"

he managed to elicit from the innkeeper a description of their last customer, and he saddled up his horse and rode off in search of him. He soon overtook Dic Spot, who was travelling on foot, and, chuckling to himself, the conjuror agreed to lift the spell. He told the young and sensible villager to remove the over-priced bill from under the table, and blessed him to make him immune to the charm. The villager thanked Dic, and then returned to Henllan... though I shouldn't think he hurried.

The Pig o' the Brook

"By magic spells the Pig o' the Brook
    The village pilferer oft took;
    The fortune of each Girl he knew,
    And if her swain were false or true;
    He'd rule the planets too, they say,
    And tell both Birth and Bridal Day:
    Could trace each Scene in People's Lives,
    And Bachelors oft helped to Wives:
    Could Dreams expound, or lay a Ghost
    In the Red Sea — with Pharoah's Host:
    Each Thought before him stood confess'd.
    Which made Folks think he was possess'd."

So John Roberts, called Mochyn-y-Nant (*Pig of the Brook*), is described in an old, undated pamphlet printed in Ellesmere. He lived in Ruabon several hundred years ago, and was much sought after as a magician. However, there is some doubt as to whether the Pig o' the Brook was really possessed of magic powers, or whether he was just a lucky conman with a gift of the gab and an instinct for things spiritual. The following story rather suggests the latter...

A rich old lady once lost a valuable diamond ring. She searched and searched all over for it, but regretfully came to the conclusion that it had been stolen. Realising that her only hope of recovering the ring was in discovering the thief, she decided to send for a magician — and the Pig o' the Brook was duly summoned.

Now, the Pig o' the Brook had had rather a slack period of late, with very few requests for his services, and he hadn't eaten in several days. He therefore decided, when he arrived at the old woman's door, that the first thing he would do was ask for three hearty meals to fill him up.

"I cannot work on an empty stomach," he explained, "but fear not, for whilst I am eating, I shall be using my powers to divine the whereabouts of your stolen property. I am never idle!" — and he sat down at the dining table.

His first meal was duly brought him, by one of the rich lady's three footmen. The sorcerer stuffed it down him, and when finished cast a glance in the servant's direction and cried: "Tis well, I have the first!"

The footmen turned pale, and after he had cleared the table he hurried back down to the kitchen, where his two colleagues were preparing the other meals. He hurried up to them, trembling with fright.

"He *is* a Cunning Man," he told them. "The Pig o' the Brook has discovered us!"

The two footmen turned as pale as their colleague, because it was they who had stolen the ring. They had no time to consider their predicament, however, because the magician was already calling for his next meal. The second footmen hurried upstairs with it. As he slapped the food up, John Roberts cried, with some satisfaction: "The second's in my sack!"

The servant dropped the tray in his dismay. When the third trembling footman served John his meal, the sorcerer cried: "My task is done; the third, thank God, is here!"

That was enough for the footmen. Convinced that the Pig o' the Brook had discovered them, they determined to try and bribe him before he informed their mistress. John retired to a little room by himself to digest his meals, or — as he told his rich old client — to "commune with the spirits", and here the footmen confessed the deed, and handed him the ring. The magician was as astonished as they were, but didn't show it.

"If you do not expose us, you'll never want for a meal again at this house," the footmen told him. That was enough for John.

"Very well," he said. "Go away, and let me think of a plan!"

When, later in the day, the old lady tentatively suggested that John do something about locating her ring, she was exasperated by a further request for a meal.

"But, this time, join me in the repast, madam," said John, "and I give you my word that we shall locate your property even as we eat."

The old woman had no option but to comply, and the three footmen brought in a goose from her own farmyard. With great ceremony, John took the carving knife from the first footman, and cut into the roast. There, inside the goose's stomach was the ring! The old woman fainted with surprise. The Pig o' the Brook wiped the diamond clean with his napkin and explained to the startled, but relieved, footmen how he had forced the goose to eat the ring earlier in the day.

"Which is why earlier I specifically asked for that goose for my tea," he said. When she recovered, the grateful old woman pressed several gold coins into the Pig o' the Brook's hand, and then scuttled off to tell her neighbours all about it. Thusly, the Pig o' the Brook grew richer by a few sovereigns and his fame spread a little further.

Huw Llwyd and the Bandits

The most famous Welsh sorcerer was Huw Llwyd. There was no doubting his credentials, for he was the seventh son of a seventh son and gifted with true magic. He was the father of Morgan Llwyd, a celebrated mystic of the Civil War period. There are many stories told about him, but because his home was in the heart of Snowdonia, there are only two from Clwyd. They both take place near the western border, in the vicinity of the once thriving little town of Pentrefoelas.

One evening, Huw Llwyd, on his travels round the country, had cause to stop at an inn at Pentrefoelas. Pentrefoelas in those days was quite a rough place, not the sleepy village it now is, because it was one of the most important market towns in North Wales. It was the meeting place for all the drovers from Gwynedd who were on their way to the English markets with the animals in their charge. There was much drunkenness, and much money changing hands, because some drovers preferred not to go into England themselves, but sub-contracted other drovers to do so. To make matters worse, the nearby village of Ysbyty Ifan was a notorious den of thieves and bandits, and they would hang around the town hoping to rob some rich drover of his gold.

Huw had just been settling down to a meal of hot broth at a quiet corner table, when four such thieves pressed themselves upon him. They pretended to be friendly, and pulled up chairs around the table, so that Huw found himself wedged into the corner. His magic powers showed him that they were bandits, and he realised that they had mistaken him for a drover returning from an English market, a drover who would naturally have his pockets full of gold from the selling of his beasts.

The bandits leered at the sorcerer threateningly, and one took out a knife, with which he began to clean his filthy fingernails in a meaningful manner. Although there was no doubting their intentions toward him, Huw was unconcerned. He was tired, and wanted to go to bed. He didn't want any trouble. However, he thought it his duty to apprehend these villains, so that they could do no future mischief. He stifled a yawn and said:

"You, gentlemen, are notorious bandits, and I can see that you are all wanted by the magistrates. I will fetch them in the morning."

The chief bandit stopped cleaning his nails, and they all gawped at their victim, astounded at his boldness. The wizard pointed at them with his finger, and he lowered it slowly to the table top. The rogues couldn't help following it with their eyes. Then, Huw tapped the table with his finger tip, and, as the thieves looked on in wonder, the wood beneath it buckled and heaved and splintered.

From out of the table burst a strange object like a cow's horn. It was a magic horn which possessed hypnotic qualities. The bandits found they couldn't take their eyes off it, and they sat there, entranced. Huw squeezed past the nearest of them and went up to bed. They were still seated there, staring at the horn, when he rose the following morning, and they were there still when the magistrates he sent from Betws-y-coed came to collect them. They only awoke from their trance when the magic horn vanished — and that was at the very moment the chief bandit felt an arresting hand laid upon his shoulder.

The House in the Shadows

On the old road between Cerrigydrudion and Betws-y-coed, close to the Denbighshire border, somewhere near Pentrefoelas, there was once a ramshackle old boarding house, low and dark and crumbling with age. It stood back from the road, overshadowed by trees, and was so named Ty'n-y-cysgodion, (*the House in the Shadows*).

Ty'n-y-cysgodion grew to have an evil reputation. People who had stayed there would speak of the strange noises they heard in their room at night, the watchfulness of small, green eyes they saw in the dark, and of money and valuables going missing by morning, although the door was locked from the inside and there was no way in or out. However, travellers continued to stay there, for it stood on an otherwise deserted stretch of a busy road, and some wayfarers had no choice but to break their journey there, evil reputation or not. And no stranger knocking at the door could feel any qualms when greeted by the two frail old ladies who owned the establishment. How could they cause harm to anyone?

This was something Huw Llwyd decided one evening to find out. He was sure some dark practises were behind the tales told about Ty'n-y-cysgodion, and he was just the man to put a stop to it if there were. The two old owners of Ty'n-y-cysgodion were delighted with the guest who called on them that evening: a tall, distinguished-looking gentleman in a military uniform, with a full purse jingling at his belt. It was Huw Llwyd in disguise, but they were not to know this.

Huw told the old ladies that he was a colonel in His Majesty's army in Ireland, on his way home on leave having just got paid, and they trilled their interest. He ordered a bowl of soup, which he found to his surprise to be quite good, and then said that he would immediately retire. Before he did so, however, he asked for a bundle of candles, because, he explained, he had got into the habit through active service of having a light burning through the night whilst he was asleep. The women happily complied, and Huw retired to his bedroom, with no intention of sleeping at all.

Huw lay awake through most of the night, lighting candle after candle as they burned down, until he began to wonder whether the stories he had heard had in fact been idle rumour after all. Then he heard a stealthy noise coming from somewhere on the opposite side of the room. He quickly closed his eyes, but continued to watch through the closed lids. In the dim light cast by the candle, Huw saw two elliptical green eyes watching him from an upper corner of the room. Then, a black cat crept out of a hole in the plaster and dropped silently to the floor. Another pair of eyes peeped out from the hole, and the first cat was joined by another. Huw cautiously felt for the sword which had been strapped to his belt as part of his disguise, but which now lay beside his bed, and which he had every intention of using.

The two cats crept about the room, keeping a wary eye on the apparently sleeping Huw. They approached his clothes, which lay draped over a chair by the bedside, and one of the animals jumped onto the coverlet, and padded gently over Huw's body. Huw's fingers tightened round the hilt of his sword. The cat on the floor pawed at Huw's trousers, and succeeded in untying the heavy bag of coins bound to it — and at that moment Huw struck! He lashed out with his sword, and the cat yowled with pain as the blade slashed through its paw. The other cat squawled with fear and, hissing and spitting, they both leapt back into the hole from which they had emerged. Huw sighed with relief. *Now* he understood the situation.

The next morning, Huw went in search of the two old ladies. But only one seemed to be in evidence. She was very polite, and she hoped the colonel had had a pleasant night's sleep? Huw said, yes, he had, thank you, and shook her warmly by the hand.

"Now, I must thank your sister for her hospitality before I go," he said. "Where is she?"

The old woman apologised, but said her sister was indisposed. Huw muttered his regrets, and opened his money bag. He took out a gold sovereign to pay for his lodging, and then drew out a couple more. He rubbed them together invitingly.

"I would so liked to have thanked your sister too," he said, and, rather as expected, the other woman came out of the shadows, where she had been hiding, lured by the gleam of the gold. Huw insisted that he shake her by the hand, but she seemed reluctant. Eventually, she showed the reason for her reluctance — her bleeding hand was swathed in a bandage.

That was all Huw needed to convince him. The two old ladies were witches, capable of transforming themselves into cats, so that they could rob their guests. Huw was a powerful enough wizard to vanquish their dark gifts, and he grabbed each witch in turn and scratched them across their foreheads with a blessed iron pin. The women wailed and struggled, but as they felt the trickle of blood run across their faces they knew that their dark powers had been drained away also. Huw took back his gold sovereign and left.

The witches, no longer having the ability to rob their guests, fell into a state of misery, and shortly their length of years caught up with them, and they died, damned and unloved. Ty'n-y-cysgodion was never occupied again, and crumbled away forever.

The Cursing Well

In a field on the northern edge of the Denbighshire village of Llanelian-yn-Rhos, a square patch of muddy earth is all that remains of what was once one of the most infamous spots in Wales — Ffynnon Elian, the cursing well. It was said that the well first sprang into being due to the prayers of the 6th Century holy nobleman, St Elian, so that he could quench a raging thirst that one afternoon afflicted him. The well was once endowed with great healing properties, and people came from far and near to be cured by its waters. However, the greed and selfishness of the visitors had the effect of souring the waters, and some time after 1723, Ffynnon Elian gained a quite different reputation — that of a cursing well.

People soon discovered the well's unique property; it would not only grant favours for good, but for bad also. Where it could remove ill fortune or illness, it could by the same token bring bad luck and sickness down upon whomsoever the user wished. The method of inflicting curses developed over the years. At first, a small piece of parchment, with the name or initials of the intended victim scrawled upon it, would be pierced by a bent pin and put into the well. In later years, the parchment would be sealed in a thin layer of lead which was then attached to a slate, upon which the initials would be scratched, and then placed in the well. One woman dropped a carved figure of marl, stuck full of pins, into the waters, so that her husband suffered terrible pains. Then, she took it out and pierced its head with a pin, so that her husband nearly went mad with agony. Only when his attitude had softened towards her did she remove the figure.

Not surprisingly, the well became greatly feared. It also became very popular, and people would travel hundreds of miles to use it. A thriving business soon built up. Many healing wells were attended by a Christian woman or a white witch to help sufferers bathing in the waters, but a black witch was guardian of St Elian's Well. She would charge people to use it. In the early years of the 19th Century, the "priestess" of the well was discovered to be earning annually as much as £300, an absolute fortune in those days.

At the peak of its notoriety, the well was in the control of the wicked Holland family (whom I sincerely hope are no relations of mine!), evil practisers of black magic who came to Wales in the 15th Century after being thrown out of their native Exeter by a populace outraged at their decadent lifestyle. The last priestess of the well was probably a Holland. She had an accomplice, John Evans, known as "Jac Ffynnon Elian", who was once apprentice to an infamous male witch from Oswestry, Dr Bennion. Jac would roam the countryside, calling on well-off, but stupid, farmers, clergymen and other men of means and would inform them that they had been "put into the well", and would therefore suffer dire ill. He would play upon his victim's fear, pretending that he was only informing him out of courtesy, so that he had a chance of having his name removed from the well and his luck returned to him.

Of course, the only way they could have their names taken out of the well was by paying more than the mythical person who had supposedly cursed them in the first place had paid to put them in. The gullible fellow would be brought to the well at midnight, made to perform a ridiculous ceremony under the watchful gaze of the priestess, and then asked to cough up with as many shillings as they thought they could get away with.

This lucrative scam went on for many years, but finally enough complaints came to the ears of the magistrates for Jac to be arrested. He was finally charged with obtaining money under false pretences in the case of an Elizabeth Davies, to whom he claimed he could cure her husband of some sickness by taking his name out of the well, for the reasonable sum of seven shillings. He was sentenced for six months hard labour, after which he turned quite religious. The well priestess was considered mad and too old to bother sentencing, and she was released. The well may have continued to attract customers to this day, had not a Victorian rector of Llanelian, righteously indignant at the effect its presence was having on his parishioners, personally filled it in. Potatoes now grow over it.

Witchcraft and Sorcery —
Bibliography

Rev. Elias Owen, M.A., *Welsh Folklore* (Oswestry and Wrexham 1896 and EP Publishing 1976).

Rev. Elias Owen M.A., *Old Stone Crosses of the Vale of Clwyd* (London, Oswestry and Wrexham 1886).

Marie Trevelyan, *Folklore and Folk Stories of Wales* (Eliot Stock 1909).

T. Gwynn Jones, *Welsh Folklore and Folk Custom* (1930, T.S. Brewer 1979).

W. Jenkyn Thomas, *The Welsh Fairy Book* (Fisher-Unwin 1907 and John Jones Ltd 1979).

Jane Pugh, *Welsh Witches and Warlocks* (Gwasg Carreg Gwalch).

Ken Radford, *Tales of North Wales* (Skilton and Shaw 1982).

Rev. Ellis Davies M.A., F.S.A., *Prehistoric and Roman Remains in Denbighshire* (Cardiff 1929).

Rev. Ellis Davies M.A., F.S.A., *Prehistoric and Roman Remains in Flintshire* (Cardiff 1949).

G. Bellys, *Howell Gwynedd* (1914).

G.J. Bennet Esq., *A Pedestrian Tour Through North Wales* (Henry Coburn Publishers 1837).

J. Gwynn Williams M.A., *Witchcraft in 17th Century Flinthsire* (Flintshire Historical Society Transactions).

D. Leslie Davies, *The Black Arts in Wrexham* (Denbighshire Historical Society Transactions).

Bryn R. Parry, *Ffynnon Elian* (Denbighshire Historical Society Transactions).

Trefor M. Owen, *A Charm From Chirk* (Denbighshire Historical Society Transactions).

Byegones.

HOLY MAGIC

The most powerful magic was holy magic — that which came directly from heaven. This was the magic wielded by the holy saints. In the 'Monsters' chapter, we have already seen how the combined might of the saints Garmon and Cynhafal served to destroy the wicked giant Benlli Gawr and his palace. They were not alone in possessing supernatural power, many of our early Welsh saints could bring about wondrous things by prayer alone — or so the stories in this chapter tell us.

Holy places, such as roadside crosses, were also believed to possess magical properties. Stone images of Christ and the Virgin Mary were visited from near and far by pilgrims hoping for a divine blessing to cure some malady of heart or body. From time to time, somebody would claim to have had visions of the Blessed Saviour or His Holy Mother, and they would be appealed upon by the common populace for cures. At the now unidentified village of Orton Matlock in Maelor Saesneg, a young girl of thirteen or fourteen named Elizabeth Acton claimed to have experienced such visions, and some accounts of them were printed as broadsheets. However, she publicly confessed to her deceptions in Chester Cathedral in 1582.

The holy wells, springs blessed by a saint, were most popularly resorted to for performing cures. In the previous chapter, it was described how St Elian, severely parched, had prayed for a spring of water, and a well had sprung up to slake his thirst. The well, since it had been brought about by the direct intervention of God, was considered very holy, and was assumed to have had divine properties (until, uniquely, it became used for evil purposes). Many, many more wells and springs which were dedicated to saints — most of them local holy men — were also believed to be efficacious in healing a variety of ailments. In fact, the worship of wells, and the belief in their healing properties, go back to pre-Christian times, to the ancient religion of the Celts. Not all wells *were* dedicated to Christian saints, as you shall see.

This chapter is a bit of a hotch-potch of stories. In common, there is some Christian basis to all the stories, and the magic which their heroes use is one which cannot rightfully be called witchcraft or sorcery. It begins with a description of some of the more famous holy wells from Clwyd. There are far too many to be described completely (that would take up another book!), but one or two, like St Tegla's Well at Llandegla, were famous for their cures and received hundreds of visitors every year.

Holy Wells

Ffynnon Degla (*Well of St Tegla*) is sunk into a field a few hundred yards south-west of St Tegla's Church at Llandegla. One midnight, a young boy stood beside the well, shivering in the dark. At his side, there came a scratching and a quivering, for under his arm he carried a black cockerel in a basket. Tentatively, the boy began to walk around the black, still water and in a high, uncertain voice he began to recite the Lord's Prayer. Three times he circled the well, and three times he recited the prayer. The cockerel fell silent.

The boy retraced his steps across the muddy field, and returned to the village of Llandegla. The church loomed above him against the night sky, and he cast an eye towards the light of the guest house where his father was anxiously waiting for him. But he steeled his nerve, clutched his basket to himself tighter, and entered the churchyard. Three times he walked around the church, and three times he recited the Lord's Prayer. Then he entered the cool silence of the church itself. He approached the altar, the figures in the stained glass staring down upon him grey in the moonlight. He placed his basket upon the floor, climbed onto the altar, and slid beneath the altar cloth.

He rested his head upon the great church bible and settled down to sleep. In the nearby guest house his father also, reluctantly, lay down to sleep. He knew that he could not accompany his child, and tried not to worry about him lying alone in the strange building, for this was how the ritual of the well must be observed. The boy suffered from fits, he was an epileptic. A few months ago his father had experienced omens of death, one after the other, all, he realised, predicting an early death for his son. But a wise man told him that his epilepsy could be cured by the holy water of the well at Llandegla, and explained to him the ritual for relieving him of his illness. They wasted no time but immediatey set off for the well from their home at Bala, and there was nothing now to do but try to sleep and wait for morning.

The dawn light woke the boy in the church first, and he ran to wake his father. He left the cockerel behind him in the church. It was later collected by the verger, who placed it with the other fowl in his garden, and fed it and observed it closely, waiting hopefully for it to die. The cure of the well worked by transmitting the illness of the sufferer into the bird he used in the ritual. If it died, the disease died with it. If not, the cure was unsuccessful. The boy and his father returned to Bala the same day, to spend a stressful week waiting for news of the cockerel's condition. But at the end of the week the message from Llandegla arrived. The cockerel had died. The boy, in fact, went on to live a full life.

It is uncertain how long this ritual for the cure of epilepsy at St Tegla's Well continued to be observed, but Wirt Sikes in his book *British Goblins* (Sampson Low, 1880) records an old man of Llandegla saying that he could remember the cocks at the well "staggering about from the effects of the fits" transferred to them. I visited Ffynnon Degla last year (1988) and was saddened to discover that what had once been a revered focus for pilgrims was now nothing more than a square, muddy patch in a field, overgrown with yellow reeds, which I had walked right past originally without even noticing.

Rather more impressive, though only recently rediscovered, is the well dedicated to St Ddier, Deifer or Deifar at Bodfari. St Deifar was a pious and gentle healer who came to live at Bodfari in the 7th Century, and used the well water for baptisms and for performing cures. The well must have had special properties of its own, for in Roman times it was dedicated to Aesupapius, the god of medicine, and was used to supply water for the summer house of the Emperor Antoninus. It was probably originally dedicated to an ancient British god of healing. Pilgrims came from far and near to worship at the well, and to have cures performed upon them, and a little stone barracks was built to house them.

There are many stories of mothers using the well to cure "peevish" children. They would dip the babes up to their neck in the water to stop them crying at night. It was said that for more elaborate cures, the well had to be circled nine times, before immersing three times in the water. A male person carried a cockerel whilst doing this, a female carried a pullet. The bird took on the illness of the sufferer, exactly as at Llandegla.

For many years, the locations of the well and the ancient pilgrims' lodging house were unknown. However, during renovations to the 17th Century Dinorben Arms public house at Bodfari during the 1950s, a deep floor was dug down to which suggested a very early Medieval origin. At one end of this old room was found — a well! It is not unlikely that the ancient foundations of the Dinorben Arms belonged to the pilgrims' lodging house (possibly even Antoninus' summer house), and that the well was none other than St Deifar's. The wells is on view inside the pub, with a glass plate covering it, and one can gaze down into its clear, now electrically illuminated waters.

Another recently rediscovered well is St George's Well, located just inside the grounds of Kinmel Park near the hamlet of St George, where England's patron saint slew the dragon. It is certainly an ancient well, for its walls date back at least as far as the Middle Ages. However, like many springs it was probably also worshipped in pagan times, for particularly sacred to this well are horses, and horses were also sacred to the Celts. Horses with distemper were brought to the well and sprinkled with its water, while the words:

"The blessing of God and St George be upon thee"

were recited. Centuries hence, the very richest of the land, who owned many horses, would choose one from the stable weaker than the rest and would bring it to St George's Well and there sacrifice it, believing that this ritual offering would serve to protect the rest of the stock.

Not every healing well was dedicated to a Christian saint, and not every holy well was used primarily for healing. Ffynnon Eflo is a spring at Abergele which does not appear to have been dedicated to anybody, and yet, in the 19th Century, it was visited by rather optimistic children who would leave old tins bathing in its waters and return weeks later expecting them to have been transformed to gold. It was also visited every Easter morning by people who wished to practice hydromancy — the use of water for divination. By performing some ancient, pagan ritual now

Within a serene glade, Ffynnon Sara still issues with water clear as crystal.

forgotten, they would attempt to discover what was to happen to them in the future.

Hydromancy was also used at an unnamed spring near Efenechtyd by a woman called Elizabeth Hughes. She took one of her undergarments, bathed it in the spring, struck it with a mallet, repeated some doggerel verse, and prayed that she might see the form of her future husband. To her shock, a hand took the mallet off her and continued to beat the garment. It belonged to a slight acquaintance of hers — or his image. She ran away in a great fright, but married him within the year.

Ffynnon Sara at Clawddnewydd near Derwen is said to be named after the white witch who tended it. Sara lived in a humble cottage beside the well and would administer to the sick people who came to bathe in its healing water. It is said that her cottage was once crammed with unwanted crutches and bath chairs. The well was considered particularly good at curing certain kinds of cancers. Ffynnon Sara is, in fact, dedicted to St Saeran, an early Irish saint, who was very active in the area and built the first church at nearby Llanynys. Sara is therefore probably a corruption of his name. A hundred years ago Ffynnon Sara was derelict but a good Christian, the Rev. Percy Cook, made it beautiful by planting many trees and wild flowers around it. It possesses now a calm and magical atmosphere, more serene than any church. I think it is the holiest place that I have ever visited.

The most famous well in Clwyd is St Winifred's Well at Holywell (*Treffynnon*). It was once known as "the Lourdes of Wales". People came from all over Britain to experience its curative power. The story of how the well sprang into being is a classic legend of the county, but perhaps no more hard to believe than some of the stories told about it subsequently...

The Legend of St Winifred

St Beuno was an old and wise saint who lived over a thousand years ago. One day he decided that he had had enough of the solitary hermit's existence and so he went to live with his sister, Wenlo, and her family at the place we now call Holywell. Their house stood on a hill above the village, and Beuno built himself a little chapel below it. Wenlo had a daughter, Winifred

The Medieval shrine of St Winifred's, Britain's most famous holy well.

(*Gwenffrewi*), a pure-hearted girl whose only joy was to serve God. The holy man took her under his wing and instructed her in the scriptures.

For many years all was bliss, but then, one afternoon, an oafish, foul-minded prince called Caradocus turned up at Winifred's house while her parents were away and rudely demanded refreshment. He slumped into a chair, all sweaty from hunting, and then caught his timid hostess round the waist as she tried to pour his wine.

"Well, aren't you a pretty lass?" he said, belching. Winifred slipped from his grasp, quite horrified, and tried to escape his lewd attention. However, Caradocus, now smitten by Winifred's virginal beauty, wanted no denials.

"I shall marry you!" he cried, lying, but Winifred was having none of it. She told him that she was already engaged, which was not a falsehood, because truly she was chosen for God. Caradocus decided that what she was unwilling to give freely, he would take by force, and he cornered the poor girl in the kitchen. Winifred tried to wrestle free from his coarse advances, but found she could not, so attempted subterfuge instead.

"Please, sir," she said, "I find myself overwhelmed by your...passion...but I am unworthy as I am, I have been slaving over a hot stove all day. Please, let me retire to my chamber for just a few moments so that I may prettify myself, make myself more desirable to you."

Caradocus was taken in by this, and the innocent Winifred, doing her best to look seductive, slipped behind a curtain covering the entrance to her room. Then, she nimbly clambered over the windowsill and ran for her life down the hill to the little chapel where her Uncle Beuno was at prayers. But as luck would have it, Caradocus glanced out of the kitchen window and saw her making her escape. Enraged beyond reason, he drew his sword and charged after her. He was by far the stronger runner, and soon caught up with her, just as St Beuno came out of his chapel to see what the commotion was all about.

Caradocus snatched Winifred's wrist and swung her round. He caught one glimpse of her terrified, pleading face and then, without a word, he hacked off her head with his sword and threw it down the hill.

The events which immediately followed seemed to happen in slow motion. St Beuno had seen the whole ghastly business and, dark fury rising up from the depths of his very soul, he uttered a terrible curse. Caradocus' brutal features became instantly transformed. They twisted and buckled, and the prince squeaked with fear. His whole body melted like wax. A pink sludge congealed on the ground, and the earth opened up a crack, so that his last remains dribbled down straight into hell. Meanwhile, the martyred Winifred's head rolled to a halt at the very foot of the hill, and from the spot where her blood touched the earth, a clear, blessed spring gushed out.

St Beuno knelt in the spring, which was gently washing the blood from the sad, golden locks, and he took up the head and carried it reverently to where Winifred's body lay slumped on the grass. He placed the head against the severed neck and offered up a simple prayer, confident that it would be answered. The head fused to the neck, and Winifred came to life.

It was said that when Winifred's Well first sprung from the ground, it ran with milk for three days, slowly clearing to the mineralised healing water flowing to this day. It was believed from that moment it was blessed with great power. It could make cripples whole, blind men see and lunatics sane. It could do anything. Once, a man was brought to the well accused of stealing a goat, a charge he hotly denied. Rashly, he agreed to bathe in the blessed water and there repeat his claims of innocence to prove himself, since the holy well would not tolerate untruths told within it. Unfortunately for him, the goat which he had not only stolen but also eaten began to bleat inside his stomach, so he was immediately take out and stoned.

One of the strangest tales told about St Winifred's Well concerns three mysterious luminous stones said to have once appeared in the fountain in the well and there played in the water for many years. They were the fascination of many hundreds of worshippers. But one local woman, driven mad by curiosity, could not resist reaching out and touching one of them. She immediately died, and the stones vanished forever. Another tradition was that on the anniversary of St Winifred's martyrdom three red blood spots would appear on the stones at the bottom of the bathing pool inside the well. However, when that learned Doctor, Samuel Johnson, visited St Winifred's Well in the 18th Century he was amused to find some men painting the red spots onto the stone early in the morning before anyone but he was about.

As well as the fantastic stories told of St Winifred's Well, there are also many accounts of genuine cures performed there for people bathing in its medicinal waters. It is still visited regularly by many people searching for an end to a suffering. The well is housed in a beautiful, elegant 15th Century shrine, constructed by the same mason as the church which stands above it, probably on the same site as St Beuno's ancient chapel.

St Werburg's Miracle

Even as early as the 12th Century, the fame of St Winifred's Well had become so great that pilgrims would travel to it from as far away as London. One such pilgrim was King Richard I, who journeyed there in 1119 after his release from a prison in Normandy to offer up his thanks. However, word of the English King's imminent arrival at Holywell had reached the ears of a group of Welsh bandits and they ambushed him on the edge of the town.

The Lionheart and his retinue made a rapid escape, hotly pursued by the Welshmen, and they were lucky enough to reach the sanctuary of nearby Basingwerk Abbey before they were captured. But they were trapped, surrounded by their enemies, with apparently no means of escape. In one direction there were hostile Welshmen, in the other nothing but the Dee Estuary. King Richard knew he had to send for help, but secretly believed that only a miracle could save him.

A message was successfully smuggled out of the abbey and taken over the border to Chester, where it was delivered to St Werburg. St Werburg thought the situation out carefully, and tried to find a solution as to how the King's reinforcements could reach Basingwerk to help their sovereign without suffering the same fate. If only they could get to the King's side without having to travel through a large area of Wales... At length, a very precise and considered prayer was sent up to Heaven, and it was not ignored.

King Richard was pacing the floor in his room in the abbey overlooking the estuary when he suddenly stopped and stared out of the window with amazement. Where before there was nothing but a sheet of grey water, there was rising up a great mass of sand and mud. Within the hour, there was formed a brand new sandbank in the middle of the Dee Estuary, joining Wales to England. And riding across it was the Constable of Chester with an army of Englishmen!

While the sounds of the ensuing battle roared outside his window, Richard remained kneeling on the floor, and offered grateful prayer after prayer. St Werburg had certainly managed a miracle. The King was shortly rescued by the constable, and they rode back to England across the divinely constructed sand bank, which is known to this day as the Constable's Sands.

St Asaph and the Ring

Queen Nest, the most beautiful woman in Wales, rose from her bath in the clear waters of the river which ran by her home and stepped, lithe and slim as a reed, onto the bank. She wrapped herself in towels and as she dried herself she sang a joyful tune. But suddenly she cried out in horror. She dropped her towels and frantically paced the river's edge. Backwards and forwards she went, over and over again, her face intent upon the ground. Then, she dropped to her knees, and clawed around in the mud. Finally, she sat down and she wept.

"Oh!" she cried. "I have lost it," and she held out her left hand and stared at it folornly. Her wedding ring was missing. This was the ancient, sacred ring given her by her husband, Maelgwn Gwynedd, who was King of North Wales. It was the ring traditionally worn by the Queens of the North, and it had been handed down over countless generations. And now, she, wretched Nest, had lost it!

At last, she roused herself and tried to face up to the fact that the ring was somewhere at the bottom of the River Elwy, irretrievable. She sighed bitterly. How could she possibly tell her husband? He would be heartbroken. She didn't think she dare. Could she ask someone else to tell him instead? That afternoon, she remembered, she and the King were paying a call on the Bishop, perhaps that kind man would do her the favour?

Now, this bishop was St Asaph, Bishop of Llanelwy (in the 6th Century), a man who was said to have shone with "virtue and miracles from the flower of his earliest youth". When he saw the distraught Nest hurrying up the path to his church he went out to greet her, and brought her inside at once. He soon got out of her what the trouble was, and did his best to comfort her.

"Go home now," he said, "and pray. I shall see you this afternoon with your husband the king and I shall break the sad news to him at the dinner table."

And so, poor Nest went home full of anticipation for the coming afternoon, and did her best to hide her left hand from Maelgwn's chance gaze. The meal at the church was a rather strained affair, with a very silent queen and a bishop doing his best to cheer along an increasingly suspicious King. After they had had soup, Maelgwn pointedly asked Nest whether anything was wrong. St Asaph decided he ought to come clean, and admitted that yes, something was indeed wrong. As gently as he could, he broke the sad news.

Well, Maelgwn Gwynedd was beside himself. The ancient ring of his family, lost at the bottom of the river! He could hardly credit it. St Asaph eventually managed to calm him down, and told him that no personal possessions, however treasured, were

In Corwen churchyard, a Medieval cross is set within a prehistoric stone, roughly decorated with enigmatic "Cup and ring" markings, seen below left.

worth a falling out with his loved one, and, after all, accidents would happen. The king was soothed enough to help comfort his now sobbing wife, and though heavy at heart, he was no longer angry.

"Let us pray for comfort, and then continue with our meal," said St Asaph. Outside the servants hovered, laden with the next course, while the bishop, and the king and queen closed their eyes, and bowed their heads over the table. Soon, they were bade to enter, and a beautiful carp, caught that very morning from the waters of the Elwy, was laid upon the table.

St Asaph cut into the fish with a big knife and offered a large slice to Nest. Something dropped out of the flesh and full upon her plate with a tinkle. Maelgwn reached forward and picked it up. It sparkled in the sunlight. He smiled. He looked at his wife, and she smiled. He turned to St Asaph, who was already smiling.

"Well," said Nest, "I didn't know fish ate rings!" And she slipped the sacred ring back upon her finger.

Llangar Church, stands on a low rise above the sacred River Dee.

Y Carw Gwyn

Where the silver Afon Alwen flows into the holy Dee, there is situated an ancient little church surrounded by fields, miles from any town or village. Although beautiful, it is a strange location for a church, and strange is the story behind its building. It is called Llangar, *The Church of the Stag.*

A community in the district of Edeirnion in the valley of the Dee determined to build a house of God to serve them, and they chose a place where several roads met, on level ground, as a convenient site. Three elders were chosen to oversee the work and they set the men under their charge to work. Many huge stones were brought from a nearby quarry and the first yard of wall was erected, just before nightfall. The men, satisfied with a good first day's work, retired for the night in their bivouacs around the work site.

At dawn, the labourers rose full of eagerness to continue their blessed task. But they were dismayed to discover that the wall that they had built had been pulled down, and the stones themselves had vanished completely! There was no explanation for the vandalism. Nothing had been heard during the night, there were no footprints around the building site, and no signs of other disturbance. The wall had simply vanished.

"This is the Devil's work," one of the men muttered.

"Then we must pray that our holy employment goes unmolested by him today," answered one of the overseers, and they all did so. However, although the building went well that day, the following morning saw the same result — all their work undone, and the stones nowhere to be seen. There was no explanation but that some supernatural agency was determined to thwart their efforts. It was the same story the next day, and the men began to despair.

The three overseers took themselves aside and tried to come to some explanation as to what was occurring. It was then that they discovered a very strange thing... each night, after every day's building work, they had each individually dreamed the same fantastic dream. They imagined that a brilliant light had appeared before them and it had spoken to them these words:

"Seek the White Stag; build your church where you see Him."

They decided that they should do as the vision bade them, and they told their workmen of their plan. Then, they separated and set off in search of the mysterious stag. All day they wandered the hills around Glyn Dyfrdwy, neither meeting with success. But, just before nightfall, when they began to consider giving up their quest, the three overseers accidentally met up on the bank of the Dee, at the point where the Afon Alwen enters it. And there they suddenly saw Y Carw Gwyn (*The White Stag*), a huge and beautiful animal, standing above them in the twilight, its eyes observing them with bright intelligence. The men started toward it, but, tossing its massive, antlered head, it bounded away into the woods.

The old men quickly returned to the building site and told their workers of what they had seen. At dawn they switched their work to the site at the confluence of the Alwen and Dee, and within short days, as if the work were being assissted by some other agent, the walls and roof rose rapidly, and the church of Llangar was completed. And through all the centuries it has survived unmolested, to stand remote, surrounded by water, blessed with a holy solitude

The Sacred Sites

When the first Christian missionaries arrived in Wales from Ireland, they faced a tough task trying to convert the populace from their pagan beliefs. When the early churches were being established, an edict carried out throughout Europe was to take over existing Celtic temples and sacred sites, and to thereby introduce Christianity stealthily into the culture. The thought was that the people were more in the habit of worshipping at a particular place rather than in any particular way, and so could gradually be made to make Christian worship a part of their everyday habit. Pagan festivals were also incorporated in to Christian ritual. Both Christmas, the midwinter festival praying for renewal of the seasons, and Easter, the festival of rebirth, are pagan in origin.

This is probably the explanation behind the story of Llangar church. The site at a confluence in the "wizard Dee" was quite possibly sacred in ancient times, and so the church was built here so as to make it easier to tempt people within its walls. Presumably, the missionaries had attempted to bring the people to receive teaching at some spot convenient to them, had met with resistance, and finally had to build their church at some accpted holy site. This seems to have happened a lot. Churches situated within circular churchyards, like Llanelidan, Efenechdyd, Llandyrnog, Tremeirchion, and churches built within ovoidal churchyards, such as Cerrigydrudion, Llanarmon-yn-Iâl and Corwen, were originally surrounded by a blessed circle of stones or trees.

Hilltops were especially sacred to our Celtic ancestors, and so some of the oldest Christian sites, Glastonbury in Somerset, for example, are situated on prominent summits. Such churches are most often dedicated to St Michael, the Archangel, who threw Satan out of heaven. He is likely to represent the original Celtic warrior deity who was at first worshipped here.

Nowhere in Clwyd shows this usage by church builders of pagan sites better than Corwen. Corwen Church is situated on a little rise above the town, and near the west door there is built into the wall a prehistoric standing stone. The stone bears the ancient name of Carreg y Big yn y Fach Rewlyd (*The Pointed Stone in the Icy Nook*) and is probably one of the supports for a cromlech, or burial chamber, the roof of which now forms the pedestal of the nearby churchyard cross. This pedestal is a large, round, holed stone bearing ritual "cup and ring markings" dating from the Bronze Age, which may point to the site having particular sacred significance. It is said that like Llangar, Corwen church was originally to be erected elsewhere, but a supernatural agency forced the work to be carried out at its present situation, with the standing stone incorporated into its structure.

The impressive Wrexham Church, with its "tower without its steeple", one of the Seven Wonders of Wales, is also built on a rise above the town it serves, and was also caused to be sited there by invisible spirits. The foundations of the church were continually demolished by night and a disembodied voice was heard to cry: "Bryn-y-Groes!" This, *the Hill of the Cross*, was the name of the rise on which they eventually felt forced to build it.

More dramatic still was the agent which forced the rebuilding of Llanfair Dyffryn Clwyd Church. At the end of every day's building work, a giant sow's head would appear and violently smash the foundations to smithereens. In this case, the spirit did not indicate where the church site should be moved to, the prudent builders simply took up pick and shovel and retired elsewhere. The farmhouse which was built many years later in its place was given the name Llanbenwch, *the Church of the Sow's Head*.

The Destruction of Llys Ellis

Out in the ever-churning waters of Colwyn Bay, twice a year can be seen just thrusting clear of the foaming waves a huge black rock, called The Shepherd's Rock. It is the last remaining peak of a drowned land, a province once rich in pasture and dominated by the magnificence of Llys Ellis, the palace of its overlord, Llywelyn.

Llywelyn was a good man, respected by his serfs, but his brother, Dafydd, was by contrast a cruel and hated blackguard. One day dawned when Llywelyn announced that he was to leave Llys Ellis for the Holy Land, to fight with the Crusaders in Jerusalem. He placed his young son in Dafydd's custody, and gave his brother the power to rule while he was abroad. Dafydd enjoyed his new found status, and he began to swagger. He filled the court with rogues and ruffians, men as cold-hearted as himself, and over the years, with Llywelyn still not returned and presumed dead, his arrogance swelled and his cruelty sharpened.

He looked with envious eyes on his growing nephew, whose inheritance was the only block to his complete and total power. One morning, the youth was found to have vanished from his room. Dafydd professed ignorance to any knowledge of his whereabouts and suggested that the boy had simply run away, in a tone which bode no argument. And the unruly courtiers accepted the explanation unconcerned.

Only one man bar Dafydd knew what had happened to Llywelyn's heir. Ednyfed, the old hermit of Llys Ellis, kept by Dafydd for his skill at playing the harp and not for any religious reason, had been praying in a corner of the ancient chapel below the palace and had hidden when he saw his lord enter with a heavy burden over his shoulder. From out of a sack he had seen Dafydd drop the unconscious body of Llywelyn's son, and had watched with horror as he had tied rocks to the boy's lifeless limbs, and had tipped him into the dark depths of the castle well. The old and feeble man was too afraid to tell anyone of what he had seen.

From this day Llys Ellis became a byword for tyranny and injustice. Ednyfed would beautifully play his harp while ignorant courtiers would ignore his efforts as they drank and debauched at Dafydd's frequent feasts, waited upon by his gentle daughter, Morwyn, a sweet-natured girl grown pale by the sight of her father's grim descent into villainy. During one of these riotous banquets, a knocking came at the palace's heavy front door. Morwyn answered it and found at the gate a grey haired travelling holy man. He was presumably hoping for hospitality.

She flushed with fear. If the courtiers caught sight of him, they would entertain themselves by setting the dogs on him.

"Please," she said, "there is nothing for you here. Please go..."

But the holy man pushed past her with surprising strength. He strode up to the banqueting table and glanced about him. A flicker of annoyance passed his weather-worn face as he noticed the chair at its head was empty.

"Where is the lord Dafydd?" he bellowed, and the feasting courtiers gawped at him in amazement. "Bring him to me!" he demanded. One of the drunken lords rose to his feet, spitting wine and meat from his mouth in indignation, and he began to draw his sword. The old man placed both hands squarely on the table, and stared the courtier full in the face.

"Go fetch your lord, and tell him this," he said.

"He doth know

"What lieth in the deep castle well —

"And Llywelyn lives the tale to tell!"

At the name, the courtier grew pale, and sheathed again his sword. All felt silent. Not one of the drunken lords dared to pass the message on to Dafydd, for fear of his rage. Silently, Morwyn slipped away to fetch her father.

In a few moments, Dafydd barged into the room, furious and befuddled with drink. At the sight of the holy man, his mouth fell open, the colour drained from his face and he trembled like a child. Now that the two stood face to face, the assembled court, including Morwyn and the aged harpist Ednyfed, could clearly see the resemblance between the two. This was surely Llywelyn, true overlord of Llys Ellis! Llywelyn spoke quietly and deliberately, and his voice seemed to fill the hall.

"You know who I am, and I know what you have become," he said. "I know too the depths of sin to which the company of this once fine palace has fallen. And I have come to warn you, to entreat you, give up your riotous ways, repent your sins, return Llys Ellis to the house of Christian virtue which once it was, before it is to late for you."

Dafydd roared in a drunken rage and lunged at his brother with his sword. Llywelyn stepped neatly aside, and Morwyn desperately held on to her father's sword arm.

"Sweet child," said Llywelyn, "what suffering must you endure in this house of infamy? Now, I implore you" — he cried to the assembled company — "repent, leave with me now..."

But the courtiers unsteadily rose to their feet, and they fingered the pommels of their swords. They began to advance threateningly.

"I warn you for the last time," thundered Llywelyn, "your Judgement Day is nigh! This prophecy I give you — when a salt-water fish is found alive in the well where you, Dafydd, murdered my son, your destruction will be imminent." And he turned and stormed from the hall. The courtiers, secretly relieved, returned meekly to their wine, and Dafydd collapsed, a dead weight in his daughter's arms.

From the day of Llywelyn's brief return, the decadence of Llys Ellis deepened. A depression had entered into the souls of Dafydd and his court, and the evil and riotous behaviour in which they now indulged had something of a desperation about it. Morwyn and Ednyfed kept from the hall as much as was possible, and spent their time praying by the little altar near the well in the basement of the palace. Summer turned to Autumn, turned to Winter, and then it was Christmas Eve. A huge feast had been prepared, and every worthless titled man from the district of Gwynedd had been invited. It was poor Morwyn's lot to wait at her father's side, leered at by the odious lords and suffering all kinds of indignities in their company.

During the evening, the vilest entertainments and debauchery took place. The banquet had been long under way when, suddenly, on the stroke of midnight, a tiny black bird smashed through an upper casement and fluttered around the ceiling, crying in a panic. It went unheeded by the drunken lords, but there was something in its cry that made Morwyn's blood run cold. For to her ears the squawking seemed to be repeating over and over again the words: *Dial a ddaw! Dial a ddaw!* The bird was a prophet of doom. "Vengeance is coming! Vengeance is coming!" it sang.

Morwyn tore from the hall and ran down the twisting, darkened steps that descended beneath the palace to the little chapel, there to warn Ednyfed. She found the old harper kneeling beside the well, which, she noticed, was steadily overflowing. He did not move at her approach, and she touched him on the shoulder, and he turned slowly round. His face was stricken.

"Our doom has come upon us, child," he murmured, and he lifted his hand from where it had been plunged in the well water and held it before her face. In it was clenched a fish, wriggling feebly and gaping wide. Morwyn looked at Ednyfed horrified. "And the water is salt!" the old man cried. They both remembered the prophecy of Llywelyn. Ednyfed threw the fish back into the well, and Morwyn grabbed him by the hand and dragged him up the stairs. Behind them, unheeded, the well suddenly bubbled and heaved and the water began to gush over its rim.

Above, in the great hall, Morwyn desperately tried to convince her father of the calamity that was to befall them, but

Dafydd was now insensible with drink, and he leered at her stupidly with his fat red face. He grasped her round the waist and attempted to pull her onto his lap, mistaking her for one of his bawds. Morwyn screamed and pulled away. She fled from the hall in disgust. Ednyfed was anxiously waiting for her at the front gate, and she flung herself upon him sobbing. At that moment a tremor rocked the palace. Ednyfed took Morwyn by the hand and pulled her out into the open country.

"Do not look behind you," he said, and he made her run across the fields. Their only hope, he knew, lay in the high ground which skirted the land of Llys Ellis. As they ran, an ominous rumbling filled the air, and tremors shook their feet. Behind them, in the palace, the lords staggered uncertainly to their feet, and were then swept to the floor by a huge wave which flooded up from the basement. The water rose with terrifying velocity, and the revellers were too affected by wine to consider their escape in time. Their screams echoed on the air, and it was all in Ednyfed's feeble power to prevent Morwyn from running back in an attempt to save her accursed father. But as she struggled in his grasp, she kept her eyes fixed upon the palace as water burst from its door, carrying bodies of the drowned with it, and then rose rapidly up, flooding in torrents from the windows of each successive storey, until finally it flowed from the very battlements.

Transfixed, Morwyn and Ednyfed watched the destruction of Llys Ellis. The walls crumbled and cracked and then suddenly exploded outwards as a mountainous jet of sea water roared out from the earth. The old man and the young girl clung to each other in their terror, but at that awful moment they heard a quiet voice address them, and there was Llywelyn, garbed in his knight's armour. He held the reins of two horses, onto one of which he threw the near fainting Morwyn, while Ednyfed mounted the other. The steeds whinnied and galloped away as the swelling sea came in a flood towards them.

On a pigh peak Llywelyn finally wheeled his steed about and he gestured in the direction from which they had fled. Before their wondering eyes there lay a beautiful bay glinting in the moonlight, a calm stretch of ocean which would never rise further, but which would never recede again to reveal the ruins of the doomed palace of Llys Ellis, nor ever throw up the corpses of its wicked occupants.

The sombre ruins of Basingerk Abbey, once the home of the ill-fated Brother Meurig.

The Sad Fate of Brother Meurig

Sad Brother Meurig was a monk of the abbey of Basingwerk at Greenfield near Holywell. He was a lonely, solitary man who went about his prayers and humble tasks without communicating with his fellow monks. He did not partake in what simple pleasures there were to be had from life in the monastery, but would roam the abbey grounds lost in thought. His only joy was in nature, and it was this that made him so sad. His life was devoted to the glorification of God, but not his heart. As he gazed over the green hills overlooking the estuary he would sigh and wonder — how could paradise ever be so beautiful? He was getting older and soon the pleasure he obtained from the Welsh countryside, its landscape, its birds, its animals, would be denied him. All would perish.

Brother Meurig would frequently take long walks in the countryside he loved so much, absorbed in thoughts such as these. One fine afternoon he woke from his meditations to find that he had wandered much further from the abbey than ever before. He had reached a beautiful green field he did not recognise. It was skirted by woods and it was perfectly level, but for a mound which stood at one corner. He had, in fact, rambled many miles from Basingwerk, to the other side of Mold, at a place called Pentrehobyn, and he was standing in the meadow called Cae Deryn Cân — *the Call-Bird Field*. However, all this was unknown to him.

He sighed, and rested himself on the mound. There was an extraordinarily serene atmosphere about the place. If paradise could only be like this, he thought. Then he gave a sadder sigh — if beauty such as this was doomed to fade in time, how could paradise continue forever?

Just as these thoughts entered his head, the peace was broken by a sweet sound, the sweetest he had ever heard. It was the singing of a bird. It was like a nightingale but with a tune so elusive, so ravishing, and with notes so pure, that the music struck him to his soul. He rose to his feet breathless with admiration and he stood transfixed. The tune seemed to go on forever and Brother Meurig listened and listened. Eventually, the invisible bird seemed to retreat into the woods and its enchanting singing faded by degrees away.

Meurig seemed to awake from a dream, and then he suddenly realised that it must be getting late, and he remembered the many miles he had to walk home. He waited for a few moments more, should the singing continue, but since all remained silent, he finally, reluctantly, set off for home. When he reached Greenfield the sun was beginning to set and he hurried to the abbey, aware that he was probably late for refectory. Then he saw a sight that pulled him up in his tracks. Silhouetted in the ruddy glow of the setting sun was Basingwerk Abbey — ruined!

Meurig gasped, stunned. Then he ran to the front door, only to find there was no front door, for the archway was bare. Staggering inside what he knew as the main hall he found instead a field of grass open to the sky, in which the first few evening stars winked down mockingly.

"No, no, it cannot be!" cried the poor monk, and he wandered distracted round the crumbling walls which snakelike marked the outline of his home of only a few hours before. He made his way to his own cell, two stones which formed a barely discernable corner, and there he collapsed and wept.

He was woken by the dawn and the dew cold upon his robe. He left the ruins and in a daze made his way to where he knew a cottage stood nearby. Perhaps the occupant could tell him what had happened — had there been a fire? But he soon became aware that more than the abbey had been transformed since yesterday. The cottage had vanished, but in its place was a village. People came out of their homes and they stared at him. He felt a tremble of fear in his stomach. They dressed in a fashion he had never seen before. They jabbered to each other in a strange language he did not recognise, and they pointed at him and some laughed. Meurig wept in the street.

An old couple left the gathering crowd and approached him.

"Please, please, tell me where I am," he said. "Where are my brothers? What has happened to the abbey?"

But the old people shook their heads. Clearly, they did not understand him. Gently they led him to a small house by the road and took him inside. Meurig was sat gently down by the fire and the old couple discussed who their strange guest might be.

"He is dressed like a monk," observed the old woman, "and surely did he not say something about 'brothers'? I think it was Welsh he was speaking, but it was so difficult to tell."

"I wonder," said her husband, "wife, do you remember that old legend told about the abbey — about that monk who one day went out for a walk but never returned? Could it be...?"

"Well," returned his practical spouse, "if this is he, after all these years he must be hungry!" And she bustled off to the kitchen.

All this time, Meurig had sat drying his robe by the fire, his head bowed, utterly dejected. He knew he was being discussed but simply could not make out the meaning of the words. Everything was so strange he began to think that he had been transported away from Wales altogether. Just then the woman returned with a bowl of porridge. Meurig suddenly realised he was very hungry.

"Here, love, eat some of this," said the kind old woman, and she gently raised the spoon to his lips. Meurig put his mouth around it.

As soon as his tongue touched the food, Meurig's face froze

and cracked, and before the old couple's horrified eyes he crumbled into dust.

(This story has much in common with the many fairy tales told about mortals who become enchanted so that they find themselves, like Rip Van Winkle, transported centuries into the future. Other examples are to be found in the next chapter.)

Holy Magic — Bibliography

W. Jenkyn Thomas, *The Welsh Fairy Book* (Fisher Unwin 1907 & John Jones 1979).

Wirt Sikes, *British Goblins* (Sampson Low, London 1880 & E.P. Publishing 1973).

T. Gwynn Jones, *Welsh Folklore and Folk Custom* (T.S. Brewer 1979).

Ken Radford, *Tales of North Wales* (Skilton and Shaw 1982).

Folklore, Myths and Legends of Britain (Reader's Digest 1973).

Marc Alexander, *Haunted Churches and Abbeys of Britain* (Arthur Barker Ltd 1978).

Thomas Pennant, *A Tour in Wales* (London 1784).

Maxwell Fraser, *Wales Vol. II — The Country* (Robert Hale Ltd 1952).

M.B. Clough, *Scenes and Stories Little Known* (Mold and London 1861).

Charles Henry Leslie, *Rambles Round Mold* (Mold 1869).

Henry Roberts, *Illustrated Guide to Corwen and Neighbourhood* (Corwen Eisteddfod Committee 1902).

Country Quest.

Chester Chronicle.

THE FAIRIES

Stories about fairies, a seldom seen race of (little) people who share this earth with us mortals, are told all over the world. Of all its folklore, Wales is particularly famous for its fairy tales.

The Welsh fairies were said to hail from a land known as Annwn, which was believed to lie somewhere underground. It was a beautiful place full of sunshine, and its inhabitants lived in fine palaces full of treasure and abundant with good food. The land was ruled over by a powerful king named Gwyn ap Nudd. Folklore tells us that there were two main groups of fairy. In England these were referred to as the Seelie and the Unseelie. In Wales, the Seelie were represented by the Tylwyth Teg or Fair Folk, who were always attractive in appearance and finely dressed. They would sometimes be encountered in great companies, perhaps singing and dancing to their own enchanting music or out on hunts riding snow-white ponies and accompanied by tiny spotted hounds.

Although the fairies are most often described as being smaller in stature than human beings, this was not necessarily so. Some female members of the Tylwyth Teg have married mortal men. They were generally well-disposed towards the human race, but it was still not best to associate with them, since they were unpredictable and in the habit of spiriting away people they took a fancy to.

Rather more dangerous were the members of the other class of fairy — the Unseelie. These were largely represented by the grotesque "little people" which would be called in England goblins, bogeys or piskies. In Wales these are called *coblynau, bwbach, pwca*, or most commonly they come under the blanket term *ellyllon*, which includes a whole menagerie of strange creatures, including the Cŵn Annwn we encountered in the Monsters chapter and the church-demolishing spirits of the previous chapter.

Another phrase used as a name for the fairies was Bendith y Mamau, which is translatable as *Blessing of Mothers*. This name was particularly common in Clwyd, but its meaning is obscure. One explanation was that it was a polite term, referring to the fact that fairies were fond of stealing human children. The more truthful phrase, Melltith y Mamau (*The Curse of the Mothers*) would be offensive to fairy ears, who were apt to take their revenge, and was rarely used.

Fairy children were apparently rather weak and sickly and so human infants were often eyed with envy. For this reason, many forms of protection were used to discourage them, and cribs were often decked with rowan wood or had suspended above them scissors or pieces of iron. The scissors would hang in the form of a cross and had the added advantage of being composed of cold iron, since iron was for some reason especially repugnant to the Bendith y Mamau. However, if a baby was left unattended, it would sometimes be stolen and taken away to fairyland and replaced with a fairy infant. This was disguised by a fairy magic called glamour so that it resembled the stolen child and was only distinguishable from its original by the fact that it was peevish and that it would not thrive, never growing bigger or learning to walk or talk. These imposters were called Changelings.

That belief in Changelings was strong even until a couple of hundred years ago is evinced by a story told by Thomas Pennant in his *History of Whiteford and Holywell*, which was published in 1796. He tells of how a couple of poor cottagers, convinced that their baby was a Changeling because it was so peevish, left it out all night under a tree called the Fairy Oak, which grew behind Downing, his house. Their belief was that the fairy parents would not allow their own child to perish, and so would return the stolen one. When they went to fetch their baby the next morning they found it lying quietly where they had left it and went away perfectly content in their belief.

The Fairy Oak at Whitford was by no means the only tree to be associated with the fairies. An enormous walnut tree grew out of a limestone escarpment at Llanddyn farm near Llangollen, and it was said by the locals that this was the place the Tylwyth Teg came to recite their wedding vows. When it was felled in 1809 it was over 75 feet high, and it claimed a victim — a sawyer engaged on the task was killed by a falling branch. Particularly popular fairy meeting places were maiden oaks. Such a tree grows out of a large barrow called the Fairy Mound, which is located behind the high brick wall of a house in Fairy Road, Wrexham. A few years ago, the *Wrexham Leader* reproduced a note written by an old woman in the 1860's in which she told of how as a little girl she used to visit this mound (which in those days used to stand in open fields) at dusk in the hope of catching sight of the fairies popularly supposed to meet there. However, they always seemed to run away whenever she drew near, though one of her friends claimed to have frequently seen "hundreds of them at a time". "According to my companion," she writes, "the fairies looked very beautiful, with frilly little wings" — a very Victorian interpretation. Interestingly enough, in 19th Century Wrexham there was a blind beggar who used to swear that his misfortune came about because he had been spying on a fairy, which in revenge for his impertinence rendered him sightless!

Whenever fairies got together it was normally for one particular purpose — to dance. Fairies were overly fond of dancing, and they were often sighted performing a kind of Elizabethan round dance, hand in hand in a circle. The poet Gerard Manley Hopkins was told by a girl, who was teaching him Welsh, that she had seen on the road into Holywell:

"three little boys of about four years-old wearing little frock coats and odd little caps running and dancing... taking hands and going round, then going further, still dancing and always coming together..."

More recently, a young girl saw "about a dozen fairies dancing round a fire" on a lonely hillside at Llangwyfan, near Moel Arthur, one early October morning. This was reported in a letter in the *North Wales Newsline* paper quite recently, the informant being the middle-aged daughter of the witness. Fortunately, neither of these informants were tempted to join in with the fairy's dancing, for this was a very dangerous thing to do. One could be carried away to fairyland, or could dance for centuries without noticing. A particularly favoured dancing spot of the fairies was Moel Fama, the highest mountain in the Clwydian Range.

Alas, fairies are not seen so often now as they once were, though reminders of their presence are still with us. Places they used to haunt may still carry their names, for example, such as Nant Ellyll (*The Elf's Brook*) at Llanfair Dyffryn Clwyd or Cae Coblyn (*Goblin Field*) at St Asaph. The foxglove is called in

Welsh Fairies' Gloves, or rather Menyg Ellyllon. Occasionally, tiny stone hammers or arrowheads are found, and these were once said to be the tools of the fairies. The Rev. Elias Owen describes minute clay pipes found from time to time in Clwyd, which were named Cetyn y Tylwyth Teg (*Pipes of the Fair Folk*), since only fairies were small enough to use them.

However, it is through the many fairy tales that have come down to us in Clwyd that the fairies have been best remembered, for here they come alive. So, let us start with an example of one of the commonest varieties of fairy tales, in which a mortal is foolish enough to accept the invitation to join in with a fairy dance...

The Fairy Dance

In isolated fields throughout Wales one can sometimes come across wide rings of bright green grass said to mark the places where the fair folk perform their magical dances. One such fairy ring existed (may still exist) a hundred years ago at Bryneglwys near Corwen, and this was pointed out to the Rev. Elias Owen while he was out collecting stories for his *Welsh Folklore* by a local farmer. The farmer said that he had himself seen the fairies dancing there, though he had never ventured too close, believing it to be dangerous to do so. He related an account of what happened to a man who had not only ventured close, but actually joined in the dance.

Many years before, two waggoners were early one morning taking some coals across the hills to the then busy lead mines at Minera near Wrexham, and they found themselves drawing near the fairy ring. From its centre came the sound of tinkling music and round and round its perimeter wheeled a score of Tylwyth Teg in a spritely dance.

"Come and join us!" called out one of the fairies in a piping voice. "Join our dance!"

One of the waggoners, enchanted by the spectacle, stepped forward to take up the invitation, but his friend backed away in horror. Not only was it ungodly to associate with fairies, it was highly dangerous, too. However, before he could react, his companion had taken the hands of two of the fair folk and had joined the circle.

"Huw, man, don't be a fool!" he cried out, but to no avail — his friend was already dancing away. Desperately, the carter entreated his friend to leave the fairy dance and to join him in taking the waggons to Minera. However, he did not dare approach too close, for fear of finding himself caught up in the fairy ring also, and his friend remained oblivious to his presence, a glazed but blissful expression on his face as he moved in time to the music. So, reluctantly, the waggoner eventually decided to take charge of both the cartloads of coal and to continue his journey.

It was dusk when he was bringing the empty waggons back to Bryneglwys and as he approached the fairy circle he found it to be empty, with no sign of his friend Huw. He called into the twilight for a little while, but finally gave up and trudged wearily home. Every morning and evening for a week the carter returned to the fairy ring in search of his friend, but his search was always in vain. Several months went by and Huw still did not reappear.

Then, one day, on the mountain not far from the circle, the carter came across a fairy standing by the path. A little warily the carter greeted it, and received a courteous reply. He wasted no time in asking after his friend, and the fairy proved to be helpful. It told him to visit a certain spot on the hill at a certain time, and there, it said, he would find Huw. Then, before the carter could thank him, the fairy turned on its heel and vanished. Trying not to be too hopeful, the carter waited until the time set by the fairy and then visited the spot it had indicated. Out of the shadows loomed a figure. It was Huw. He looked happy but confused on catching sight of his companion.

"Hello," he said. "Where are the waggons?"

He had no recollection of what had happened or that he had been missing for several months.

The Dangers of Fairy Music

One fine, warm summer's evening, a man was returning from a day's work to his home in Pentrefoelas when he heard on the still air the muted sound of beautiful music coming from some distance away. He stopped and listened. It gradually drew closer and he could discern voices, high and sweet, accompanying the

Pentrefoelas, Clwyd's fay town.

tune. He stood enchanted, allowing the music to wash over him. A minute or two later the source of the music became apparent as around the corner of the road stepped a long line of little grey-clad folk, each playing an instrument, each singing at the top of its clear, lovely voice. When the strange procession began to file past the wondering man, it stopped and one at a time the little singers began to earnestly entreat him to join in their singing and become one of their company. Now, Pentrefoelas was well-known as an especially fairy-haunted town and the man was thus acquainted well enough with fairy-lore to know to refuse the invitations.

"No thank you," he replied, more firmly and steadfastly with every offer. Finally, the fairies gave up and continued their procession, breaking into two groups and filing away in different directions, still singing at the top of their high, clear voices. For a long time, the man stood and listened to the enchanting music of the fairies receding into the distance, until the last note had died away. Then, like one awaking from a dream, he shook his head and continued on his journey home.

That this resident of Pentrefoelas was more than sensible in refusing the fairies' offer to join them is evident in a story about a young boy who once lived in the small village of Cwm near Rhyl. The boy was one morning sent out on an errand to borrow some domestic implement from a neighbour. An hour later he had not returned, and he was still missing when dusk began to creep in. By the next morning, the whole village was out looking for him. But it was many, many years before he was seen again.

On a morning very like the one on which he had left, he appeared at the open door of the cottage, clutching in his hand the object for which he had originally been sent. He had, he explained, when out followed some beautiful people playing delightful music. Then he had remembered his errand and came home. He would not believe that years had elapsed between the start and completion of his task, but he could not argue when a mirror was held up to his face. The reflection showed not the image of a smooth-skinned lad, but the wizened, grey features of an old, decrepit man. The last few remaining years of his life were spent in desperate searching for the place where he might be taken under the fairies' enchantment once again. But he never found it.

Rewards and Fairies

Although fairies were a somewhat uncertain folk with whom to have dealings, they could be generous and were always willing to repay a kindness done them. This was discovered by an old lady of Pentrefoelas. She was an old widow of the village, a little aloof from her neighbours, who was proud, hardworking and very particular about tidiness. She kept the house in good order with the hearth well swept and everything dusted and in its place.

Every evening she swept the floor clean and put a few fresh peat upon the fire to keep it going through the night. Then she retired to bed.

One night, the Pentrefoelas fairies, out on one of their nocturnal rambles, came across the cottage and stole inside. They were most impressed with the cleanliness of the home and were delighted with the warm fire. It was just the sort of place that they liked, and they decided to stay the night. The next night they returned, but this time, before departing, having enjoyed themselves greatly, the fairies left as a token of thanks a bright new shilling on the hearth in gratitude.

In this way, the woman bettered herself considerably, and became the envy of all her neighbours, who, when they perceived she payed for all her groceries only with new shillings, determined to find out where they came from. Unfortunately, in her simplicity, the old woman was more than happy to tell them, but in so doing she broke the trust of the fairies, and they were offended. They never more visited her home, and so never again did the widow find a shilling on her hearthstone.

Something similar occurred to an old man at Corwen, although in this case the fairies seem simply to have taken pity on him, rather than repaying him for any particular favour. The man was a shoemaker by trade, but due to infirmity and failing eyesight he had to give up this occupation and look for work elsewhere. He obtained a job at a tanyard at Pen-y-bont, which was several miles from his home, and was forced to walk daily to work, since he could not afford lodgings. One morning, he spotted a green circle on the grass and lying in it was a silver coin. Hardly believing his luck, he picked it up and continued on his way to the tanyard. Every morning from then on a silver coin was waiting for him in the fairy ring.

The daily silver coin added to his weekly wage soon took the man from poverty to comparative wealth. His wife begged to know from where he got the money, but he would not say. Eventually, however, after repeated questioning, he gave in and told her. As soon as he had done so, the fairies relinquished their help. No more coins were found in the ring. Shortly after, the old man died, but one hopes that this was merely coincidence and not the result of fairy revenge.

Fairy Dogs

There was once a farmer of Clocaenog near Ruthin, a hard-hearted, bad-tempered man, who one day came across a little, pale, pink-spotted dog near his farm, looking bedraggled and whimpering quietly. Since it had no collar round its neck and there was no-one else in sight, he reasoned that it must be a stray and so took it home with him. He did not treat it well. Instead of drying it down, he left it out in the cold, and he scarcely fed it. When he remembered it at all he simply used it as the brunt of his frequent outbursts of temper.

After a few days, there came a knocking at his door. On opening it, he was greeted by a diminutive old man who inquired after his missing dog. He accurately described it and stated the day on which it had become lost. The farmer, putting no value on the unfortunate animal, handed it over. The old man was evidently pleased at recovering his dog, and, smiling his thanks, passed the farmer a large bag of coins. Then, bowing low, he walked off into the forest. The farmer jingled the bag up and down happily, and congratulated himself on taking in the dog in the first place.

However, he was not to know that by this time the fairy (for so he was) had realised the unkind way in which his pet had been treated, and when the farmer opened the money bag his chuckles of self-satisfaction ceased. Where there had been coins, now there was nothing more than a load of damp, brown leaves.

These fairy dogs seem to have become lost quite frequently. Greyhound-like, they were hunting dogs, and often became separated from the pack when out on fairy rides. The Clocaenog farmer was in fact treated quite leniently compared to another person who behaved cruelly towards a stray fairy dog.

This was an old hag from Pentrefoelas. She had just been raising a stick to the animal, when she was discovered by the fairy huntsmen who had been out searching for it. They retrieved the hound and with icy politeness asked the woman this question:

"How would you rather travel home? Below the wind, in the wind, or above the wind?"

Now, if she had answered "above", she would have found herself rushing through the airless space above the clouds, and if she had replied "in", she would have been flown pleasantly home on the breeze. Unfortunately, not quite knowing what to reply, she plumped for the most uncomfortable choice of all: "below the wind". Instantly, before she had time even to scream, an invisible force grabbed her by the ankles and dragged her away, six inches from the ground, at a terrifying speed through bogs and brambles and gorse until, stunned, dishevelled and bleeding, she was dumped outside her front door.

It is not surprising then that when another old lady stumbled across a lonely, strange little dog wandering around Pentrefoelas village a few months later, she decided to treat it somewhat better than had her unlucky predecessor. She took it home with her, placed it on a plumped up pillow by the fire, fed it on buttermilk and generally made much of it. The next morning, a little man came to the door of the old woman's cottage and was extremely grateful when his pet was returned to him unharmed and happy. The old woman knew she was in the presence of a fairy and hopped from one foot to the other in expectation of the gift she might receive. The little man grinned at her.

"Which would you prefer," he asked, "a clean cowyard or a dirty cowyard?"

This was not what the old woman had expected at all, but being a practical soul she thought about it and reasoned that since a dirty cowyard normally meant that there must be lots of cows using it, she ought to reply the latter. So she did, and immediately, for every cow she had had before, there were now two in its place. So, she prospered, and lived, so they say, happily ever after.

Fairy dogs are not the only animals to have visited the mortal world from fairyland, as can be seen in the next story.

A Fairy Cow

Left undisturbed by the Forestry Commission's extensive re-planting of the Clocaenog Forest, the remains of prehistoric dwellings, called hut circles, can be found in a clearing located about half a mile north of Pont Petryal bridge, which is midway between Llanfihangel Glyn Myfyr and Clawddnewydd on the B5105 road. Many years ago these primitive enclosures were the home of a strange and wonderful animal which bore the name Y

Beneath the still waters of the Alwen Reservoir is drowned Llyn Dau Ychen, where the Fairy Cow returned to Fairyland and an old harper performed at a Fairy Court standing by its shore.

Fuwch Frech, or the *Freckled Cow*. This was a handsome milch cow and was so named because she had a white coat covered all over with pink speckles, a sure mark of an animal from fairyland.

She was as gentle as a lamb and would allow any person to milk her. In fact, it did not seem to matter how often she was milked or how much was taken, for there was always more than enough left for the next person. One could take any vessel of any size to the Fuwch Frech and it could be filled. She never ran dry. For this reason she was loved by the local men and women, and her name is still known in the district. There is a Ffynnon y Fuwch Frech (*Well of the Freckled Cow*), where she was said to have slaked her thirst, and the remains of an old byre called Preseb y Fuwch Frech (*the Freckled Cow's Crib*), where she gave birth to a pair of mighty oxen called the Ychain Banawg, which we encountered in The Devil in Cerrigydrudion Church story in an earlier chapter. The nearby farm of Cefn Bannog is named after them.

Naturally, with so much fresh milk always available to anyone who ever needed it, the people who lived in the surrounding countryside grew healthy, and prospered. One year, when a famine struck North Wales, the Fuwch Frech was needed more than ever. However, an old hag, outcast from her neighbours, grew jealous of all this health and prosperity and determined to put a stop to it. So, she took a riddle or seive and proceeded to milk the poor animal dry. She milked and milked, and of course it all poured through the holes in the riddle. Finally, even the Fuwch Frech could give no more. The old hag cackled in triumph, and scampered away before anyone could find her.

After being so abused, the Fuwch Frech decided to leave the world of mortals forever. She set up a distressed bellowing and started off for a lake lying four miles away. En route she was joined by her offspring, the Ychain Banawg. All three of them disappeared beneath the surface of the water, never more to be seen. The lake (which now lies drowned beneath the Alwen Reservoir) was named Llyn-dau-ychain in their memory.*

The Strange Benefactor

A young man who lived in a remote cottage on the isolated Hiraethog Moors one day had business many miles away in Denbigh. He set off very early one morning before it was quite light. The narrow grey road stretched on for many miles and all about him was spread anonymous moorland, completely empty. Then, as he approached the little Brenig bridge (now on the edge of the Brenig Reservoir) he was surprised to see a man standing on the opposite side. He could not understand where he could have come from, since the road had been deserted only moments before and there was nowhere for him to have hidden.

As he stepped onto the bridge the young man could discern the stranger in more detail. He was a tall gentleman, dressed in grey clothes offset by gold buttons and big gold buttons on his grey shoes. It was then that the traveller felt an uneasiness come over him, an uneasiness which became a cold, irrational fear the closer he got to the mysterious man. This sensation of fear became so strong that the boy almost considered turning and running for home, except that he was so many miles from anywhere that the idea seemed quite ridiculous. But the strange

---

*   This is an alternative version of how the lake got its name to that told in the story I called 'The Devil in Cerrigydrudion Church'.

Pont Brenig, once standing in open moorland, now enclosed by Forestry Commission conifers.

man smiled at the boy and he gave a nod of his head. Then, he stepped off the bridge and into the bog — and he vanished beneath it!

The young man was nervous about having to pass that way to Denbigh again, but each time he did so he found at the place where he had encountered the mysterious man a small pile of money and valuables waiting for him. Who his strange benefactor was no-one found out, but it seems likely he was a resident of Annwn.

The Favoured

Perhaps the luckiest man to encounter the Fairies was Tomas Morus. He lived at Pen-y-nant near the fairy stronghold of Pentrefoelas, and was on his way home late one night after attending Llanrwst fair when he suddenly came across a group of

Tylwyth Teg dancing in a ring. They greeted him and asked him whether he would like to join them in their dance. He saw no reason to refuse (being rather proud of his dancing) and accepted.

"Come with us then to our dancing place," they said, and led him some way over the hill to a fairy ring near the farm of Hafod Bryn Myllt. They immediately began to dance, Tomas with them, little spotted fairy dogs in the centre, capering in time to the music. Time seemed to slip by and suddenly dawn was upon them. Tomas apparently danced well, for he was invited to join the fairy dance the following night.

"Come here and dance with us tomorrow night and you shall be rewarded with treasure for your company," one of the fairies told him. "However," it warned, "do not reveal to anyone our dancing site or the origin of the gold we shall give you, or all will be lost to you."

Well, Tomas Morus was a simple labouring man and could not resist the temptation of gold, so he agreed. And for many years following he danced every night with the fairies and every morning he went home with gold and costly presents under his arms. He gave up his job at the farm and lived in comfort.

For all this time, he remembered the injunction made upon him by the fairy and never revealed the source of his wealth or the location of the fairy ring. However, one fateful afternoon when he was more than usually drunk, Tomas blurted out his secret to a nosey and particularly persistent neighbour. That evening he went as usual to Hafod Bryn Myllt to dance with the fair folk, but he found the fairy ring deserted. A handful of cockle shells he found scattered around the perimeter, but nothing else was to be seen. Tomas had seen the last of his generous benefactors. Perhaps he should have been grateful nonetheless, however, for as we have seen in an earlier tale, it was normally a dangerous thing to dance with fairies.

The Midwife's Adventure

Several centuries ago, a well-known Denbighshire midwife was startled from her slumbers by a furious knocking at her cottage door in the middle of the night. She jumped out of bed and hurriedly dressed. She had become used to such disturbances in her career — babies never seemed to arrive at convenient times.

"I'm coming, I'm coming!" she called out as the knocking urgently continued. She threw a shawl about her shoulders and opened the door. In the doorway stood a finely liveried footman, who directed her to an elegant carriage waiting outside her cottage. As soon as she had settled herself in it, the carriage was swept away at breakneck speed through the black countryside. Shortly it drew up at the entrance of a beautiful mansion which she could not recall having seen before. She was shown into a sumptuous room in which, on a little bed, lay the woman she was required to attend. By now, the midwife had come to the conclusion that she was in the presence of a fairy. However, she stayed mum and discharged her duty well. She was later borne home in the swift carriage with many valuable presents lying about her in recognition of the services she had rendered.

A few months later, the midwife visited Ruthin fair* and there, to her surprise, she caught sight of the little woman she had attended flitting from stall to stall and performing many purchases. Despite their limited acquaintance, the midwife could not resist addressing the lady, and boldly stepped forward and asked after her. The woman seemed surprised and annoyed at the midwife's presumption, and instead of replying asked: "What, can you see me?"

"Why, yes," answered the midwife.

"With which eye?" inquired the fairy.

"Well, I suppose with this..." said the midwife, placing her hand over her left eye. The fairy immediately reached forward and touched that eye, and to the midwife's astonishment, she vanished. It was only some days later that the midwife realised that her left eye was now permanently blinded.

---

*   Ruthin Market was popularly considered a favourite haunt of the fairies. It was said that if business went well, it was because the fairies were present.

The Mysterious Palace

Shon Robert was an old and famous harper whose dextrous playing of Cymru's national instrument had won him much acclaim. He was invited to perform at many parties. One evening, he was asked to a gathering at the great house of Llechwedd Llyfn in the neighbourhood of Cefn Brith near Cerrigydrudion. His playing was so beautiful and delighted the dancers so greatly that it was late before the dancers finally disbanded.

At about midnight, Shon eventually began to make his way home across the bare mountain, a little silver jingling in his pocket. As he passed the lake called Llyn-dau-ychain (see 'A Fairy Cow') he was taken aback to see, illuminated in the bright moonlight, a magnificent palace standing by its shore. He stopped and stared in wonderment, putting down his harp and scratching his head — he was sure he had never seen such a building there before. However, he continued on his way and soon reached the entrance of the mysterious court. Here he was hailed by a footman who stepped out of the doorway and invited him to enter.

He agreed to do so, and found that a grand ball was taking place within. The ballroom was magnificently furnished, each article of furniture being constructed of solid gold. A waiter offered Shon a golden cup of wine from off a golden tray and he drank it gratefully. The richly dressed guests gathered round the old harper and, to his astonishment, one of them addressed him by name.

"Will you not play for us, Shon Robert?" he was begged.

"Gladly!" he replied, feeling inspired not only by the splendour of his surroundings but also by the warmth of the wine settling in his stomach. He quickly set up his harp and immediately his nimble fingers were flicking over the strings, skilfully plucking out a lively tune. A loud cry went up amongst the assembled people and, grabbing partners, they at once set to dancing. The merrymaking continued all night. Shon took the opportunity of laying his hat upon the floor and it was soon filled with gold coins deposited by the grateful guests. At last, as dawn began to creep in through the windows, the dancers one by one left the hall. Sighing with satisfaction, an exhausted Shon picked up his hat laden with gold and poured the contents into a leather bag in his pocket. He then searched for something to lie on, found a couch, and stretched out for a few hours sleep.

He awoke with the sun in his eyes. He rolled over on his side and buried his face in heather. He sat up sharply and found himself on the bare mountain, overlooking Llyn-dau-ychain twinkling under the noon sky. Of the palace there was no sign. Hurriedly, Shon pulled the leather bag from his pocket and, his heart in his mouth, drew out... worthless cockle shells. And then he knew for certain it was fairies, not humans, he had been performing for the previous night.

Changeling

It was a warm, golden August afternoon. Every able-bodied person from Llanfwrog, near Ruthin, was out in the fields gleaning the corn, including a young mother and her new baby. She placed the sleeping infant under the sheaves of wheat and went to work. Shortly, a band of fairies stole up from the woods on the edge of the field and silently approached the child. While the mother was concentrating on her labours, her back turned, one of the fairies quickly snatched it up and ran away with it. Another fairy replaced it with one of their own weakly children, made, with the use of the fairy-magic called glamour, to look identical to the stolen infant.

When the mother came to collect her still sleeping baby she did not notice any difference. However, after a while, she began to realise that something was amiss. The babe she was nursing did not thrive. It did not grow, ate little, and would not try to walk. Eventually, the grieving mother ran to the hovel of the old village wise woman, and there tearfully explained her fears.

"Are you sure the babe is yours?" asked the wise woman. Then she whispered into the young mother's ear a plan to discover whether, as she herself suspected, the baby was in fact a changeling. The young mother returned to her house and pretended nothing was the matter. She smiled innocently at the child and it stared back coldly. She ferreted about in the rubbish heap and she brought out an egg shell, in which she placed some yeast, hops, barley, sugar and water. The baby raised an eyebrow.

"The men will soon be in from the fields," she murmured, as if to herself. "I shall brew them all some beer in this eggshell."

"The baby sat up, its cold blue eyes open with surprise. He cried out;

> *"Mi welais fesen gan dderwen*
> *Mi welais ŵy gan iâr,*
> *Ond ni welais i erioed ddarllaw*
> *Mewn ibin ŵy iâr."*

Which means:

> "I have seen an oak having an acorn
> I have seen a hen having an egg,
> But I never saw before brewing
> In the shell of a hen's egg."

The changeling had given itself away. With a cry of triumph, the mother snatched it up and took it off to the river. It is a well-known fact that although the Tylwyth Teg frequently covet our children, they will never stand idle while one of their own is being maltreated. So, the woman stepped onto a bridge which spanned a particularly rough stretch of river and, crossing halfway, dangled the changeling over the parapet until it started squealing with terror. Then she dropped it.

Back home, she found her own dear child chuckling contentedly in his cot. And somewhere in the depths of fairyland sat a very disgruntled and very wet fairy baby, back with its own, disappointed mother.

The Orphans

Near the little village of Llangadwaladr, nestling between the folds of the remote Berwyn Mountains, lies a field called Cae Castell. In this field stands a large tumulus, which, judging by the name Cae Castell, is probably an overgrown castle mound. On this mound was once upon a time found two naked young boys.

They were strangers. No-one knew their names nor where they had come from. More peculiarly, they could not speak a word of Welsh or English, or any other recognisable language. They were assumed to be of fairy stock, and the matter caused much wonderment round about. The mound was named from this time Bryn y Meibion, *the Hill of the Sons or Youth*. Whatever their origin, however, there could be no doubt that the two boys were lost orphans and in need of help. The kind family then living at Sgwennant Farm, on whose land the mound stood, took the children in and brought them up as their own sons.

It is assumed that they made good, brought up as Welshmen, perhaps marrying and having families of their own, since nothing more is heard of them. Is it possible that their predecessors still live on in the area, fairy blood running in their veins?

The Fair Bride

There once lived a shepherd boy, I shall call him Gwyn, who lived at Hafod Garreg Farm, Pentrefoelas. He was a comely, good-natured lad but because he spent all day every day doing no more than tending his father's sheep, he was also a little lonesome. The sheep grazed down by the shore of a lake in an isolated spot miles from any household and normally unfrequented by anyone other than Gwyn.

It was with some disbelief, then, that the youth, one misty morning, caught the sound of someone weeping nearby. He stopped to listen to make sure he was not imagining it, and found that the sobbing came from behind a stack of fresh cut peat by the lakeside. Silently, he crept through the mist and peered round the side of the mound. Sitting on a small pile of turf was a maiden, crying into her hands. Gwyn stepped forward and she looked up. She was the most beautiful girl Gwyn had ever seen. She had a dainty, slender figure and long golden hair which cascaded down her back to her waist. Out of an exquisitely pretty face gazed a pair of enormous, blue, tearful eyes. Shyly, the girl smiled a tentative smile and hung her head. Gwyn, feeling that he was already in love, sat beside her and gently put his arm around her in the hope that he could be of some comfort. Soon, it was obvious to both young people that each was becoming very attracted to the other.

However, before either had the chance to say anything of their new-found love they were startled by the sudden appearance, from out of nowhere it seemed, of an ancient man with a long white beard and severe countenance. He loomed above them. The girl cried out in dismay: "Father!" The old man grabbed her by the wrist and led her into the mist. Dazed, Gwyn jumped up in pursuit, but they were nowhere to be seen. The beautiful girl and her aged father had simply vanished.

Daily, Gwyn returned to the spot by the lakeside where he had discovered his new love, but constantly in vain. His heart grew heavy with each new day's disappointment, but he tried to retain some hope that one day he would find the beautiful maiden and that although, as he had now guessed, she belonged to the Tylwyth Teg, she would one day be his bride. He did not know it, but his longing was fully reciprocated. The fairy maiden (whose name, unfortunately, has not come down to us) spent many hours sighing and weeping for the brief love she had been denied.

One morning, after many desperate attempts, she managed to elude the watchful gaze of her father and once more made a journey to the Upper World. There she met Gwyn, and his cry of joy echoed around the hillsides. The girl's father had quickly noticed her absence, however, and before the young couple even had time to kiss, he materialised before them. He glared furiously at Gwyn and extended his hand to his daughter in a silent command. But the girl drew back and shook her head. There followed a long exchange between father and daughter in a language Gwyn could not understand. In his own language he begged and begged the old man to let him take his daughter to wife.

Eventually, the old man realised that the love between his daughter and the young man was true, and that Gwyn was in earnest. Speaking in Welsh, he told the overjoyed Gwyn that he agreed to allow the marriage to take place, and that he would even supply a dowry of a large bag of gold coins. However, he put forward one condition. If Gwyn should, maliciously or otherwise, strike the fairy girl with cold iron she would return immediately to the Otherworld. Gwyn felt it a reasonable, if strange, request and he and his fairy bride were married the very next day.

All went well for many years, they lived a happy life together in the smallholding Gwyn had bought with the dowry, and they had several children. One year, a few days before the Festival of the Saint of Capel Garmon, Gwyn decided to try and capture a pair of wild ponies he had often seen grazing on the nearby hills, in order to sell them at the fair. He and his wife set out early one morning in pursuit of them. However, they were very nimble as well as wild and constantly eluded them. Just as Gwyn thought he had drawn close enough on horseback to throw a bridle over one, it would suddenly duck and weave and dart away. So, finally, in exasperation, Gwyn lost his temper and threw the bridle with all his might after one of the colts. Tragically, his wife rode into its path and the bit, which was made of iron, struck her on her bare arm.

Immediately, husband and wife realised that the condition of their marriage was broken. Before either could react, the bride's father materialised between them with a host of fairies. He took hold of his daughter and with a look of despair she was dragged away. She was not even allowed time to say farewell to her children.

The Minstrel Fay

In the days before it became ruinous, there lived at the ancient castle of Dinas Brân in the Vale of Llangollen a maiden named Myfanwy Fechan. Her father Ednyfed was lord of the castle, and she was renowned as one of the greatest beauties in Wales. Not surprisingly, she had many suitors. One of them was Ifan, her father's bard. Ifan was a man of mystery. No one knew his history, where he came from or who his family were. He always wore the simplest of clothes, which were always made of the finest cloth. It is said that:

"Ifan's eyes were as black as jet, his face was femininely fair, and his transparent skin was tinged with the beautiful, but fatal hue, which brightens the cheeks of those already doomed to the consumptive fiend, who flatters while he destroys. He was slightly formed, but exquisitely moulded, and so light was his footstep that his tread was scarcely heard, so that he obtained the application of the Minstrel Fay."*

*   All quotes in this story are taken from the version told in *A Pedestrian Tour Through North Wales* by G.J. Bennet, 1837.

Indeed, many could not help but believe that he had come from fairyland, his songs were so fair. Every evening he would set his harp beneath the casement of Myfanwy's room and would sing out his love for her. Myfanwy would gaze down upon him, tears of pity in her eyes, touched by his love, but, alas for Ifan, she could offer him no more than her esteem, for her heart was already given to another.

In her father's company was a valiant young knight, Hywel Einion, to whom she was betrothed. He was strong, handsome, brave, but also sensitive and possessed of an artistic spirit. He was deemed "the greatest ornament of chivalry". His love for Myfanwy was as deep as hers was for him, and he could not help but feel a rising jealousy as he watched Ifan performing in Ednyfed's hall, singing in a voice of heart-tugging sweetness the saddest of ballads, all the while his eyes upon the object of his love — Myfanwy. And poor Hywel could hardly fail to see the expression of sorrowful affection in his dear one's eyes, and he misconstrued it for love.

As the day on which Hywel and Myfanwy were to be married

Dinas Brân, scene of the Minstrel fay's final performance.

approached, Ifan's songs became more beautiful and more painful to hear, and he would not give up hope that his love may after all be proven not in vain. On the eve of Myfanwy's wedding day he, for the final time, set up his harp beneath her window, and he began to play.

"My Alban steed is white with foam,
    And drops his arched neck;
    The flood, the mountain, moor and glen,
    He cross'd without a check!
    Oh listen, while my harp I strike,
    And rouse its sweetest tone,
    And hear the language of a heart,
    Which beats for thee alone!"

But Myfanwy did not come to the window. Unknown to Ifan, she was standing just behind her curtain, tears flooding down her lovely face. She dared not look upon the fair minstrel, for the pain it would cause them both. Ifan kept his eyes fixed upon Myfanwy's casement, and raised his head to sing another verse.

But then he heard a sound behind him, and turned to face an outraged Hywel Einion. He had been so nervous about the following day's wedding that he had been unable to sleep, and had been out for a moonlight stroll. His feet had brought him to his bride-to-be's garden — and who should he find there but the accursed minstrel! He drew his sword.

"Take thy 'Alban steed', villain, and ride away," he said, "or God help me, I shall run you through!"

Ifan smiled at the angry young knight disdainfully and made no move. In a rage, Hywel made to grab the minstrel by the shoulder, but gave a cry of alarm. Where Ifan should have been, he held instead in his hand an aspen branch. The minstrel had vanished!

With feelings of fury mixed with fear, Hywel ran to fetch his horse and he summoned two of his squires. He was determined to ride down the minstrel, and to put an end to him. He and his squires rode all night through the black countryside, but although often they believed they caught a glimpse of the minstrel's white palfrey turning this corner or that ahead of them, and frequently heard his silvery laugh echoing on the wind, they at last had to admit defeat, for Ifan could not be found. Hywel returned weary to his bed, to catch an hour or two's sleep before rising again to dress himself in readiness for the ceremony of his marriage to Myfanwy Fechan.

All through the ceremony Ifan did not reappear. Hywel was greatly relieved, but Myfanwy Fechan could not help but feel concerned, and her father Ednyfed was quite upset — Ifan was to have accompanied the ceremony with his harp, and to have performed at the banquet afterwards. He had never let down his lord before. However, there was more to concern the court on this most joyous of days than the mysterious non-appearance of a minstrel. Finally, the moment came when the young newlyweds were to depart. Surrounded by friends and family and decked with flowers they made their way arm in arm to the castle entrance, and the great doors were swung open. On the threshold stood Ifan.

Myfanwy gave a cry of alarm, and a gasp of mutual shock rose from the courtiers. Ifan looked close to death. His skin was grey and waxy and lacked the youthful bloom that it had once possessed. His eyes were sunken and dull. His clothes hung on him like rags.

"Ifan, my minstrel, where have you been?" asked Ednyfed, but he received no reply. Ifan pushed his way past the company and into the hall. Myfanwy followed, Hywel loitered by the door. Ifan unslung his harp from around his back and set it in its accustomed place at one end of the banquetting hall. He gazed upon the worried face of the woman he loved and he began to sing.

> "My Fanwy Vechan! brightest maid,
> In scarlet robes and gold array'd!
> My Fanwy Vechan! fairest fair,
> That ever breath'd the mountain air!
> For thee do spirits pine and fade,
> As blossoms in the chilling shade,
> Debarr'd from Phoebus' genial light,
> Sink victims in the withering blight.
> My Fanwy Vechan, hear my prayer!
> Thy lover's — *tho' a child of air*!
> May peace on earth and bliss above,
> Wait on the mortal whom I love!
> My outward form of misery
> Tells what the spirit feels for thee!
> Farewell, farewell! No more the pride
> Of sweet Dwrdwy's mossy side,

In distant vales I'll breathe my woes
And seek, ah vain, vain hope! repose!
Ah!, could I die, I'd not repine
If Evan's name might live with thine."

From the commencement of his haunting song, Ifan's form grew fainter and fainter, and the light from the torches and candles illuminating the hall began to fade. Suddenly, before the horrified eyes of Myfanwy Fechan, he disappeared, and the harp fell with a clatter on the stone floor. Myfanwy slumped beside it, dead to the world.

Today, the stone which is situated at the upper end of the banquetting hall in the ruins of Dinas Brân is sometimes pointed out as being the place where, for the last time, Ifan rested his harp, to sing 'The Minstrel's Knell'.

St Collen in the Fairy Court

St Collen, the founder of Llangollen, was one time a monk at the famous abbey of Glastonbury in Somerset. While he was there he felt that he wasn't doing enough to serve God and his fellow man, so he left and spent many years wandering the countryside bringing the gospel to the common people left in ignorance. However, he became so disenchanted by the evil state of the world that he decided to become a hermit, and he shut himself away in a rude cell at the foot of a hill in what we now call Valle Crucis, *the Vale of the Crosses*.

After he had been here a time, he heard voices outside his door. One voice said to the other:

"Our Lord, Gwyn ap Nudd, is truly a fine King, ruler as he is over all the Fairies and all of Annwn."

St Collen was furious to hear such pagan pride on his own doorstep, and he shot outside, startling two finely dressed small men.

"How dare you speak like that of the fairies," he barked. "They are agents of the Evil One. Hold your tongues!"

"Hold *our* tongues?" repeated one of the little gentlemen in great hauteur. "Put forth thy tongue again and see what you get."

This sounded worryingly like a threat, so Collen retreated

back into his cell, deciding to have no more to do with these two examples of the wickedness of man. But at dawn the next day he was abruptly woken by three loud knocks at his door.

"Art thou within?" called a voice.

"Aye...aye..." Collen blearily replied.

"Then come outside. My Lord Gwyn ap Nudd requests your presence in his court atop this hill. He would speak with thee."

Collen stuck his head beneath his pillow and ignored the request. At dawn the next morning the three knocks came again at his door and a voice asked if he was within.

"Go away!" he demanded.

"Gwyn ap Nudd still requests your presence," persisted the messenger, but he was again ignored. The third morning, the request had an additional clause.

"My Lord Gwyn ap Nudd once more requests your presence in his court. He would speak with thee. Please come... or it will be the worse for thee."

This time, Collen decided to get it over with. He threw on his rough gown and took the precaution of filling a flask full of holy water, which he attached to his belt. The messenger turned out to be every inch as finely attired as the two men Collen had admonished previously, and as diminutive. He led Collen up the hillside, and there, to the saint's amazement, stood a magnificent palace which had certainly never been there before. In the forecourt dallied pretty maidens and handsome youths riding snow-white palfreys. In the hall a huge table was laid for a feast, with all manner of rich food and goblets of sparkling wine. At the head of the table a noble lord of impressive bearing sat upon a massive throne.

"Greetings, holy man," smiled the lord. "I am Gwyn ap Nudd, welcome to my court."

"Pah!" said Collen.

"Will you partake of some food... drink?" — a goblet of wine was offered him by a retainer.

"No thank you," replied Collen with stiff politeness. Gwyn ap Nudd's brow darkened, and he seemed annoyed.

"Are you not impressed?" he demanded. "See my servants" — he gestured expansively to the retainers, all liveried in suits of blue or red — "are they not the finest you have ever beheld?"

"Aye, they be fine, such as they are," replied St Collen. "Red for burning, blue for cold!"

And with that, he unstopped his flask and sprinkled holy water all around him. In a flash, the fairy court was gone. St Collen stood alone on the crown of an empty, green, windswept hill.

Tudur and the Ellyllon

Many, many years ago, there lived in the Vale of Llangollen a young shepherd named Tudur ap Einion, who tended his father's sheep on the green slopes of the hill which is crowned by Dinas Brân. Halfway up this hill there is a hollow cut into the steep ascent, and here Tudur would round up the flock before herding them down to a sheep-pen at a farm in the valley. One afternoon, just as dusk was setting in, Tudur was as usual climbing the hill to where the sheep were grazing, when he was startled to hear his name called as he descended into the hollow. On an outcrop of rock sat a tiny man.

"Greetings, Tudor ap Einion!" he called in a reedy voice.

"Hallo," replied the young shepherd, staring at the strange little figure. The man was dressed in a smock of birch leaves, his breeches were woven from moss, and on his feet were shoes made of beetle wings.

"Are you fond of dancing, Tudur?" he asked.

"Yes," replied the shepherd boy, who was indeed very fond of dancing.

"Well, look," and the little man produced from behind his back a stringed spoon and a tiny bow. It was a kind of tiny fiddle. Tudur had never seen a fiddle before. In Llangollen and all the neighbouring villages the harp was used for dances. As if in demonstration, the little man put the instrument under his chin and played a little jig. Tudur was astonished and delighted, he had never heard such music before. He could already feel his foot beginning to tap.

"If you wait around for a bit, you will be able to see some really splendid dancing," he was informed when the man stopped playing. He did not have to wait long. As the warm russet of dusk gave way to the cold blue of twilight, through the heather filed a procession of beautiful little people.

"Fairies..." muttered Tudur under his breath, for certainly they so appeared. Each was fair of form and countenance and

Two figures descend into Nant yr Ellyllon, "the Hollow of the Goblins", below Dinas Brân.

they were all dressed in pink or blue or white. One after the other they bowed low to Tudur and the fiddler, and then they solemnly formed a circle. Immediately, the little man began to play. The music was delightful, the dancing moreso, and Tudur was entranced. After the dance he was asked "Will you not join in?" but he shook his head. He was very tempted, but he was afraid that dancing with fairies was an offence against God and it was something his mother had often warned him against as a small child. The dancing continued, each more gay and spritely than the last, and at the end of each dance he was invited to join in. Finally, he threw restraint to the wind and leapt into the circle. But then a horrible change came over the scene...

The beautiful fairies shimmered before the shepherd boy's eyes and in their place appeared a host of animals — goats, pigs, dogs, cats — all ugly and deformed. The fiddler's face darkened, horns sprung from his temples, and his beetle wing shoes cracked apart to reveal two hoofs. From the back of his breeches grew a long pointed tail. With a shock of horror, Tudur realised that he was face to face with the Devil, and it was the Devil's music to which he was dancing! He realised too that it was not fairies with whom he was dancing, not the Fair Folk, at any rate, but with their darker cousins the ellyllon — *goblins!*

Desperately, he tried to leave the ring, but to his dismay he found that his feet would not obey him. They continued to dance, around and around at a desperate pace. With a cackle, the Devil fiddler vanished, and the goblins scuffled away, hideous grins on their beast-like faces. But poor Tudur continued to dance. However much he cursed his bewitched feet, it made no difference. Round and around and around he danced, and it went on all night.

Naturally, while all this had been going on, Tudur's master was wondering what had happened to his sheep. At break of day he decided to set off up the hill in search of them and his errant shepherd lad. He found his flock contented on the hillside, but down in the hollow he was taken aback by the bizarre sight of his shepherd boy twirling round and round by himself in the heather.

"Master!" Tudur cried weakly. "Help me, make me stop."

"Stop yourself... by Heaven!" returned his bemused master. As soon as that holy word was uttered, the charm was broken. Tudur collapsed in an exhausted heap. It was several days before he was able to finally tell his tale, and today the hollow where his adventure took place is still known as Nant-yr-Ellyllon — *Hollow of the Goblins.*

The Bodfari Goblins

In the previous tale we were introduced for the first time to another class of fairy to those we have met before. The ellyllon or coblynau were a grotesque form of the beautiful, elegant Fair Folk. Frequently ugly, always small, they belonged to a lower form altogether, with none of the background of fine palaces or courtly etiquette associated with the Tylwyth Teg. In 1757, a group of such creatures greatly frightened some children at Bodfari. The encounter was reported in the autobiography of the Rev. Dr Edward Williams, a well-known clergyman, who was born at Glan Clwyd, Bodfari, in 1750 and died in 1813. He was one of the children involved. He tells the story so well that I felt it would be a mistake to attempt to rewrite it. Here it is, then, in his own words:

"On a fine summer day (about midsummer) between the hourse of 12 at noon and one, my eldest sister and myself, our next neighbour's children Barbara and Ann Evans, both older than myself, were in a field called Cae Caled near their house [Llanelwyd], all innocently engaged at play by a hedge under a tree and not far from the stile next to that house, when one of us observed on the middle of the field a company of — what shall I call them? — *Beings,* neither men, nor women, nor children, dancing with great briskness. They were full in view less than a hundred yards from us, consisting of about 7 or 8 couples: we could not well reckon them, owing to the briskness of their motions and the consternation with which we were struck at a sight so unusual. They were all clothed in red, dress not unlike a military uniform, without hats, but their heads tied with handkerchiefs of a reddish colour, sprigged or spotted with yellow, all uniform in this as in habit, all tied behind with the corners hanging down their backs, and white handkerchiefs in their hands held loose by the corners. They appeared of a size somewhat less than our own, but more like dwarfs than children. On first discovery we began, with no small dread, to question one another as to what they could be, as there were no soldiers in the country, nor was it time for May dancers, and as they differed much from all the human beings we had ever seen. Thus alarmed we dropped our play, left our station, and made for the stile. Still keeping our eyes upon them we observed one of their company starting from the rest and making towards us with a running pace. I being the youngest was the last at the stile, and, though struck with an inexpressible panic, saw the *grim elf* just at my heels, having a full and clear, though terrific view of him, with his ancient, swarthy and grim complexion. I screamed out exceedingly; my sister also and our companions set up a roar, and the former dragged me with violence over the stile on which at the instant I was disengaged from it, this warlike Liliputian leaned and stretched himself after me, but came not over."

The terrified children ran to the house and told their story. Several men went to investigate, but Cae Caled field was found deserted.

Bwlch-y-Ddâr.

A Goblin on the Bed-Post

Mr Bonnor was a kindly man. He was quite rich, owning many of the small homesteads and cottages at Bwlch-y-Ddâr, a hamlet on the southernmost border of Clwyd, south of Llangedwyn, in the 19th Century. In the capacity of landlord he was particularly well-respected. He was always keen to see that his property was in good repair and that his tenants were comfortable, and not in want of anything to which they were entitled. As a result, the inhabitants of Bwlch-y-Ddâr held Mr Bonnor in high esteem, valuing him above the local magistrate or even the Lord of the Manor as a man to turn to in time of trouble. Old Robert Jones knew just what to say, then, when he discovered some unwelcome guests in his home...

Robert had been startled awake one night by a noise in his room (there was only one room in his tiny cottage, a kitchen with a bed in one corner). Sitting on his bed-post, as bold as anything,

165

was an ugly little man vigorously playing a fiddle. A whole host of little people were cavorting around the room with gleeful abandon.

"What? What?" spluttered Robert in bewilderment. "Who are you?"

"We are the spirits of the air," replied the fiddler, grinning.

"But what do you want here?" asked Robert.

"To dance, my friend, to dance!" cried the fiddler, and played even faster. "And what's more," he continued, "we will be coming back tomorrow."

Old Robert was outraged.

"Oh no you won't!" he exclaimed. The fiddler stuck his tongue out and continued playing.

"I shall go and tell Mr Bonnor — then see if you dare."

The music stopped, and the little folk left at once. The threat had presumably been sufficient, for they never returned. Robert slept undisturbed for the rest of his days.

Fairy Mining

Since Roman times, and probably before, the landscape of Clwyd has been pock-marked with mines, used to extract a variety of minerals — lead and coal most importantly, but also zinc, copper, spar and even silver and gold. It is not surprising, perhaps, that deep under the ground, nearer their own home, fairies made themselves known to the men who toiled in the dark and, to them, alien environment. They were rarely directly encountered by the miners, but their presence was often felt.

A repeated knocking on the wall of a gallery was said to be due to a fairy indicating the source of a particularly rich ore seam, it being said that the sound was that of the fairies themselves mining it. For this reason, they were commonly called nocars or *knockers*, and mining would normally be started up where they indicated. It was believed that in this way many important lodes were discovered. Occasionally, the knockings were more complicated, including the sounds of boring, pumping, waggons trundling, even blasting. Little tools — picks, spades and the such — were sometimes found in the deeper recesses of some mines, and even mines managers up until the 19th Century, or

Llanferres Church.

even later, did not doubt the existence of their fellow, supernatural, workers down below. Yellow, sticky petroleum deposits found filling the cracks of the limestone in lead mines was called fairy butter, and was used as an oitment to cure rheumatism caused by the subterranean damp.

One or two miners were blessed with a special intimacy with the nocars, and being favoured with their help were able to extract far more ore than anyone else. One such man was Dic Humphries, a collier at Rhosllannerchrugog in the Denbighshire coalfield in the late 19th Century. He always worked alone and at night, and succeeded in cutting out such phenomenal amounts of coal that there was never any doubt in the minds of his colleagues that he worked with the help of the fairies. He was nicknamed Y Safiwr Mawr — *the Great Undercutter* — and was quite a local celebrity in his day.

I mentioned earlier that the fairy miners were rarely observed. In fact, there is only one story to my knowledge where one is seen in Clwyd. The background to the encounter is that a mining engineer was out exploring for lead-bearing lodes in the vicinity of Llanferres a few miles from Mold, when to his surprise he came across an unmapped cutting in the shale near the church.

He asked around the village and a man told him that it was his brother who had cut it, and he explained the reason why.

The man's brother had been coming home late from work one summer's evening, when he decided to rest for a short while under a hedge near Llanferres Church. Suddenly, a short distance before him, he saw the top of a ladder push its way out of the ground, to a height of three or four feet. Then, up the ladder climbed a little man, dressed exactly like a miner, in big boots and rough breeches, with a felt hat on his head holding a tallow candle. Over his shoulder he carried a pick. The mine-fairy did not see the man's brother but walked away to a hedge opposite and disappeared beneath it. Well, this could only be considered an omen, a sign that rich minerals lay beneath, and so after the story was recounted, a great many people invested their money in cutting the area. Unfortunately, as it turned out, although there was some lead present, the vein was actually rather poor.

"Where is My Son, John?"

One quiet evening, in a little wood called Coed Cochion near Llanfair Dyffryn Clwyd a man sat resting his back against a tree and watching a foxes den. He had seen the fox enter, and had laid a bag over the entrance, its mouth stretched around it and secured. Sooner or later, the animal would come out and be bagged. The man smiled. A farmer would always part with a few pence for a killed fox, and that would pay for his beer that night. Suddenly, the bag started to twitch and then rustle, as something thrashed about inside it. The man instantly leapt forward and secured the bag's mouth, then threw it over his shoulder and set out for the village. He had not gone very far when he heard a voice call out somewhere behind him:

"Where is my son, John?"

It was dark now, but he was not frightened. Presumably someone was out searching for a lad who had wandered from home. He heard the voice again.

"Where is my son, John?" it repeated. A little further on the voice came once more.

"Where is my son, John?"

The man was being followed. And then the bag over his

shoulder wriggled furiously.

"That's my father calling me!" piped up a little voice from inside it. The bag was dropped immediately. From out of its mouth scampered a little man in red. And scampering much faster in the opposite direction was the would-be fox-hunter.

(Very similar tales to this one are told as taking place at Gwyddelwern, south of Ruthin, and at Cwm Pennant, Llandrillo.)

The Invisible Riders

Cyffylliog parish, four or five miles to the west of Ruthin, was haunted by a tribe of invisible sprites whose delight it was to take horses from their stables and to ride them all night on wild hunts. They were driven half to death through heath and bog until dawn, when they were finally returned to their stalls. When their grooms came to fetch them the next morning, they were found in a filthy state, trembling with exhaustion.

A farmer writing into *Byegones* describes how he caught a colt, with the intention of breaking it in, and was told by his groom that the animal had obviously been ridden by the fairies the night before. He asked his groom how he knew this, and the groom pointed out the horse's mane had been plaited — something the Invisible Riders were wont to do to all their steeds.

"Oddly enough," writes the farmer, "the mane had been plaited in a wonderfully artistic manner."

An invisible entity once terrified a man half out of his wits in the 1850's when he was out walking across the Denbigh Moors. An unseen force suddenly grabbed him and dragged him through thorns and bushes until he lost consciousness. He awoke to find himself bleeding, his clothes in tatters, and he was perched precariously on the edge of a precipice.

Jack O' Lantern

Every county in Britain and every country in Europe has stories about the Jack O' Lantern, also called Will O' The Wisp, or, by the high minded, ignis fatuus (*foolish fire*). These were fairies which took the form of little balls of marsh gas to lead people astray across bogs and moors. Jack O' Lantern was often seen around Marford, a pretty village near the Cheshire Border. In the 1830's, a father and son one day found themselves lost on the marsh, and after wandering around aimlessly in the dark for some time glimpsed a light flickering faintly some way off. They thought it was a farmhouse window and headed towards it. It took them quite a while to reach it and just as they did so, it vanished. They took another step — and tumbled into a ditch.

Jack was considered a little servant of the Devil, sent to trap drunks. They would blearily follow him, thinking him to be their cottage window, but he would always lead them astray so that they would fall into a ditch or a bed of nettles. Then he would laugh scornfully over them. Jack O' Lantern was particularly fond of playing around the grounds of the austere Trevalyn Hall at Marford, which was also where the more orthodox members of the Tylwyth Teg held their carnival.

Gwragedd Annwn

Gwragedd Annwn means literally *Women of the Underworld*, but refers specifically to a particularly otherworldly kind of female fairy who haunted pools and lakes. Any Tylwyth Teg woman whose home was beneath still water might properly be referred to as a Gwraig Annwn, but the term was usually used when referring to the same sort of disturbing apparition as was encountered by a young man out walking one day from Diserth to Rhyl on the north coast.

It was a fine summer's day, and the youth felt blithe and care-free as he strolled along the green road, looking forward to reaching Rhyl, where there were many amusements, holidaying young ladies, and the sea. In a short while, he was overtaken by a beautiful lady dressed all in white. He greeted the woman politely, stammering with a sudden shyness. She smiled a lovely white smile, and replied kindly. Soon they were in conversation, and the boy wondered at her grace and charm. He had no idea who she was, but assumed she was some young lady of a nearby manor just out enjoying the countryside and the sun. He felt very flattered she should take any notice of a humble man like himself, and he was more than a little attracted to her. Then they began to pass by a pool of water by the side of the road, and to the youth's surprise the lady smiled and said farewell. Then, before his terrified eyes, she burst into flames! The flames conflagrated into a molten ball of fire, which disappeared beneath the surface of the water with a loud hiss. The boy was enveloped in a cloud of steam, and he fainted dead away. He never walked that way to Rhyl again!

Just as weird, but perhaps even more frightening, were the beings who lived beneath Pwll-y-wrach on Flint Mountain. They are described in the next story.

John Roberts' Death

Before it was built upon with housing estates, Flint Mountain, near old Flintshire's county town, was a wild and desolate spot, sparsely populated. Those who did live there knew that they were not alone: the area was inhabited by a tribe of strange and powerful ellyllon who appeared "in human and other forms" and were given to declaring, or sometimes warning of, future events destined to happen in the neighbourhood. Their main base seemed to be the lonely pool of still water called Pwll-y-wrach (*The Hag's Pool*), a spot which tended to be avoided, especially at night.

One man to encounter the spirits of Pwll-y-wrach was a farm labourer named John Roberts — and he was unlucky enough to receive an unbidden and frightening fortelling of his own death. It happened one early morning during the winter of 1852, just as Roberts was setting out for work. Stepping out his front door, he was taken aback to find a mysterious youth standing directly in his path, blocking his way. He asked the boy his business but received no reply. Shrugging his shoulder, he put out a hand to

The mysterious Pwll-y-Wrach on Flint Mountain.

push the youth away.

Immediately, to his inexpressible terror, he felt himself hurtled into the air, where he was flown at horrible speed across the fields to Pwll-y-wrach. He was thrown into the mud at the pool's edge and a great weight landed upon him. His face was held down until it was touching the surface of the water. The man struggled desperately, but it wasn't until some time later, when dawn broke and a cock was heard to crow at a nearby farm, that he was suddenly released. The ellyll, still in the form of a youth, stood astride him, eyeing him impassively.

"When the cuckoo sings its first note at Flint Mountain, I shall come again to fetch you," it told him.

John Roberts died the following May. He had been carrying out some building repairs at Pen-y-glyn on the mountain, when a wall fell and crushed him. A young woman who had witnessed the accident said that it had happened just as she had noticed a cuckoo come to rest in a tree nearby. Strangely, when the body was carried away to Roberts' home, the cuckoo had followed, singing from tree to tree all the way to the front door.

The Bwbach of Carreg-y-doll

Perhaps the most fearful of ellyll once inhabiting Clwyd were the goblins of Llanasa. Half a mile north-west of Llanasa church, near a house called Tŷ Gwyn, a seven-foot high stone stood atop a tumulus. Due to the presence of a hole drilled through its upper part, it bore the name of Carreg-y-doll (*the Holed Stone*). The stone was given a wide berth in daylight and avoided altogether after dark, for it was believed the barrow on which it stood was the home of evil goblins — bwbach — who guarded fiercely a valuable treasure hidden there. Their mindless gibbering could often be heard emanating from within.

One day, the strong men of the village succeeded in gathering together sufficient courage to attempt to demolish the stone, in order perhaps to vanquish the demons. Armed with pick and shovel, in a band they cautiously approached the monolith. As they drew near, the sky suddenly went dark. Towering black clouds formed above them from nowhere and a gale blew up, buffetting the men from side to side. Flashes of lightning threw the stone into stark relief, and then the rain came down, so heavy that they were drenched through in seconds. Some of the men downed tools and fled. They were shortly followed by the rest.

That evening, a stranger was passing through Llanasa. As he passed Carreg-y-doll he perceived its silhouette faintly illuminated by a ruddy glow, apparently given out by the stone itself. He decided to investigate, and as he got close he could hear an eerie sound, as of the pained whimpering of some animal, coming from beneath it. He stepped up to the stone. Immediately, he was gripped by a powerful force. It felt as if two enormous hands had grabbed him by the shoulders. He was lifted off his feet and thrown against the side of the barrow. He struggled wildly, but the invisible force held him fast. His ears were filled with the fearful sound of an insane gibbering and his eyes were blinded by a red light. The earth seemed to open up around him, and he felt himself being dragged beneath, down and down into some black place...

The next morning, the stranger was discovered, wandering around and around near the stone in a delirium. He muttered over and over again something about a terrifying place full of evil-faced goblins and weird cacklings, and sights which had obviously petrified him, but which thankfully he never fully described. After he recovered, he seemed to have forgotten his experience and never spoke of it again.

No-one is now sure of the location of the Hole Stone. It was pulled down from its barrow some time ago, it is unknown when, and believed to have resided for a period in the yard of the Red Lion Inn in the village. It is possible it was broken up for building stone. When the tumulus was ploughed in the 19th Century huge slabs of limestone were removed from it and an earthenware vessel was found smashed. No treasure was then discovered. Perhaps the Hole Stone was thrown down by treasure-seekers hundred of years ago. If so, what did they then find beneath it?

The Fairies — Bibliography

Rev. Elias Owen, *Welsh Folklore* (Oswestry and Wrexham 1896 & E.P. Publishing Ltd 1976).

T. Gwynn Jones, *Welsh Folklore and Folk Custom* (1930 & T.S. Brewer 1979).

W. Jenkins Thomas, *The Welsh Fairy Book* (Fisher Unwin 1907 & John Jones Ltd 1979).

Wirt Sikes, *British Goblins* (Sampson Low 1880 & E.P. Publishing 1973).

John Owen Huws, *Y Tylwyth Teg* (Gwasg Carreg Gwalch 1987).

Rev. Ellis Davies, *Prehistoric and Roman Remains in Denbighshire* (Cardiff 1929).

Ellis Davies M.A., F.S.A., *Prehistoric and Roman Remains in Flintshire* (Cardiff 1949).

Thomas Pennant, *History of Whiteford and Holywell* (London 1796).

G.J. Bennet, *A Pedestrian Tour Through North Wales* (London 1837).

G. Bellys, *Howell Gwynedd* (1914).

Ken Radford, *Tales of North Wales* (Skilton and Shaw 1982).

Lynn Davies, *Aspects of Mining Folklore In Wales* (1972).

Chris Barber, *Ghosts of Wales* (John Jones).

Melville Richards, 'Studies In Folk Life', *The Supernatural In Welsh Place Names*, editor G. Jenkyns (Routledge and Paul 1969).

Byegones.

The Wrexham Leader.

North Wales Newsline.

SPIRITS OF THE DEAD

It has been said that the greatest mystery in life is death. The universal fear of death and the fascination with what, if anything, succeeds it are powerful stimuli to the imagination. It is not surprising, therefore, that folklore is rich with stories concerned with the possibility of an afterlife. It is a worldwide belief that spirits of the dead may on occasion return to haunt the living.

In Wales it was once firmly believed that ghosts were abroad between midnight and dawn. No sensible Welshman would ever stray from his door between those hours. Only on Christmas Eve was it safe to do so, for on that night restless spirits were forbidden to appear on Earth. However, it was a different story on Hallowe'en (*Nos Calan Gaeaf*), for then ghosts held their carnival. In the Vale of Clwyd on every Hallowe'en night spirits would take the form of little black pigs and they would haunt stiles, spinning and weaving in the darkness. To quote an old rhyme:

> *"Hwch ddu gwta,*
> *Ar ben pob camdda,*
> *Yn nyddu ac yn gardio,*
> *Pob glan gaua'."*

Which translates as:

> "A short-tailed black sow
> On every stile
> Spinning and carding
> Each All Hallow's Eve."

Why the spirits should appear as black sows, or why they should spin or card, isn't certain, but it seems to have been a fairly common apparition. You may recall the giant sow's head which destroyed the church at Llanfair Dyffryn Clwyd, described in the "Holy Magic" chapter. A black sow would regularly emerge from an old ruin near Cernioge Mawr at Pentrefoelas and it would follow people down the lane leading past it. If

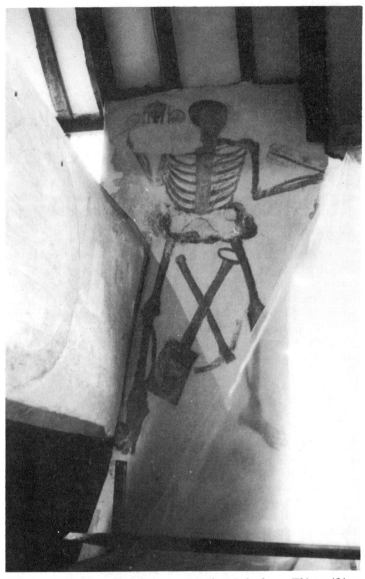

The fear of death has always been strong in the minds of men. This terrifying image has recently been uncovered, painted onto the wall of Llangar Church.

The cries of murdered children still echo from the water relentlessly flowing beneath Holt Bridge.

anyone attempted to strike it their staff would simply pass through without connecting, and the apparition would continue on regardless, until it disappeared of its own accord.

There are several reasons why a spirit might return to haunt the living. The person to whom it had belonged having met a sudden death, especially murder, was one common reason. This is why shrill screams can sometimes be heard at midnight coming from beneath the ancient bridge over the River Dee at Holt. They are made by the ghosts of two young boys, heirs to the estate of Dinas Brân during the reign of Edward I, who were drowned in the swirling waters beneath the bridge by their evil guardians. At Llanasa two other young children were brutally murdered some time in the distant past and their murderer buried their bodies beneath a bed of thyme growing behind the cottage in which they had lived. In 1891 it was said that although the murder "occurred many years ago, and no thyme has grown in the gardens since... yet, people walking past have frequently smelt the strong smell of thyme".

Self-murder was also likely to make a spirit restless on earth. A young woman who hanged herself at the now demolished

Brymbo Hall near Wrexham to escape a forced marriage made her presence known in the house for many years after her death. Her spirit would wander the hall opening doors and windows and producing icy blasts of wind. At one time the bodies of suicides were not allowed to be laid at rest in consecrated ground and they were instead buried at lonely crossroads. There is for this reason a tradition that crossroads were always haunted by spirits at night.

War and battles, the causes of so many sudden, violent deaths, could produce literally whole armies of ghosts ready to terrify the living. The 17th Century writer Robert Parry described how in 1602 at Nant-y-ffridd, a deep gorge near Bwlchgwyn, Wrexham Maelor, there was seen:

"2 or 3 thousande armed men a hors backe with banners displayed marchinge in warlike manner where as indeed there was no such thinge but some apparition or forewarninge of liklyhoode. And yet that was verefyed by 8 or ixen persons some of them of credyte that all iontly saw the same."

Another old tale tells of a young couple becoming lost in a fog-bound wood near Llangernyw, west Denbighshire, and hearing all around them the alarming sound of a bloody battle taking place, with the crash of steel on steel and the screams of dying men, although they could see nothing whatsoever of the cause. At Rhewl, north of Llangollen, the ghosts of the army of Prince Llywelyn, which was slaughtered there by Henry III in 1244, haunted the vicinity in the form of little goblins. Every night they would emerge from Coed-y-gadfa (*Wood of the Battle*), the scene of their defeat, to plague the cottagers who lived nearby. An old woman who lived on the ege of Coed-y-gadfa was employed to enter the wood at dusk carrying a large pan of fried rabbits' and frogs' legs, which she waved about around every tree. It was believed that the meat in the pan smelt just like bodies burning on a battlefield, and it would thus scare the ghostly goblins away.

Sometimes spirits would refuse to shuffle off this mortal coil because of some business they had left unfinished when alive, or because they felt bound to impart some message to a relative. This was particularly common if a sum of money had been left behind and undiscovered. The owner's spectre would often hover about the treasure's hiding place or would attempt to guide some lucky, though probably terrified, soul to it. In the days of hard cash and highwaymen and footpads valuables were frequently secreted in some safe place, only to remain unclaimed due to some misfortune falling on the owner. At Abersilio, Rhewl, a lady traveller hid a quantity of jewels in a stocking behind a beam in the room she was renting at an inn, but died before she could retrieve it. Her wraith haunted the room for many months after, and it was only when the stocking had rotted away and the jewels had fallen out onto the floor and so discovered that she was able to gain peace.

The final reason a spirit might remain restless was that the owner had been so wicked during life that it was barred from Heaven and was instead bound to earth forever. One Dafydd Salusbury, a relative of Sir John Salusbury, the slayer of the Denbigh Dragon, had been so evil during his life that his spirit is now condemned to ride on his white horse round and round the village where he lived, Llanrhaeadr-yng-Nghinmeirch, near Denbigh, moaning horribly until Judgement Day.

A kind of spirit peculiar to the Welsh are the teulu or *family* spirits. A member of a family who had died might remain with his relations for several months as an apparition before finally departing for Heaven. Nothing unusual was thought of this, and it still happens now. I spoke to a man during my research who told me that as a young child he saw his grandfather and his great-grandfather in his house for some time after their deaths; his grandfather used to stand at the top of the stairs, his image growing fainter over succeeding weeks, until it eventually vanished.

Poltergeists are a phenomenon we now closely associate with ghosts. "Things that go bump in the night" have been known and recorded for centuries, and now much research is being carried out by physicists as well as psychic investigators on how exactly they manifest themselves. However, as far as folklore is concerned, poltergeist activity was not seen necessarily as being a product of ghosts or spirits, but was often put down to other supernatural agencies. At the farmhouse of Bodeugan near St Asaph a poltergeist wreaked havoc during the December of 1812. It smashed pots and glasses, bombarded the house with bricks and pig dung and drenched the family with water. To quote a letter from the tenant to the farm owner:

"we went to bed about 10 o'clock saturday night and it began to kick and pinching the servants and pulling the bed cloaths to the floor and the two woman along with them, and has done great deal of damages, and if it will continue we must leave the House..."

The tenant was convinced that "some malicious persons had been with the conjurers" at Denbigh, and that the farm had been cursed with witchcraft. Another poltergeist haunted the farm of Cyrchynan Uchaf, owned by Edward Jones, the man who was followed by 'the Black Hound of Destiny' described in the 'Monsters' chapter. The slates on the roofs of some of the farm buildings were ripped down by an invisible entity at night, and replaced by the following morning. However, Mr Jones did not put the blame on either spirits or witchcraft. He presumed it to be the work of "the little folk".

Other kinds of supernatural phenomena were believed to foretell death. Of these the one most commonly believed in in Wales was the Cannwyll Corff or *Corpse Candle*. This was a small light like a candle which would glow about the house of someone destined to die, or would follow the course to be taken by the unfortunate's funeral procession. If the doomed person was a female the light was coloured blue, if it was a male it was coloured red. Sometimes the Cannwyll Corff appeared as the image of the dying person carrying the light. Other times it took the form of a skull with a light issuing from it.

In the south of Clwyd, a man was returning to his home at Melin-y-Wig from nearby Betws Gwerful Goch one night when he noticed before him a little light playing about in the road. He had first taken it to be a lantern, but as he approached it he realised that no-one was carrying it. It floated through the air of its own accord. The man was alarmed to see it turn into the lane leading to his home, and he hurried past it and slammed the door. To his horror, the little light passed straight through it and it then hovered about on the ceiling for a few moments, directly beneath a servant's bedchamber. The following morning the servant was found to have died during the night.

Another phenomenon warning of death was the phantom cortege, the apparition of a funeral procession appearing some days before it actually took place. A dramatic example was encountered at Corwen last century. A man strolling into the town one evening suddenly found himself in the middle of a crowd, being physically pushed back by the mass. He recognised many people but they did not seem to see him. They were all dressed in mourning clothes and were all singing, though he could not quite make out the song. He realised that it was a funeral party and that they were following a coffin. It proceeded to the parish church and then vanished. A fortnight later a friend of his died in Corwen, and he arrived late for the funeral. Because he was late, he found himself pushed back by the crowd that had already gathered, and he then realised that the scene was horribly familiar. Similar occurrences are recorded as having taken place at Ruabon and along the banks of the Clywedog River near Wrexham.

At Llangernyw there was a spirit called Angelystor or "the Recording Angel" which haunted the church every All Hallow's Eve and would intone in a deep voice the names of all the parishioners who were to die in the coming year. The local tailor, Shon ap Robert, who was considered a wit, scoffed at the existence of the spirit and one Hallowe'en processed to the church to prove it a myth. However, as he arrived at the door he heard a voice call "Shon ap Robert!" from the empty church.

"No, no, I am not quite ready!" he cried, but, ready or not, he died that coming year. At Gwyddelwern near Ruthin on Hallowe'en the churchyard was haunted by the ghosts of all the parsons who had ever served there. Young people would make solitary expeditions to the churchyard at midnight in the hope of encountering one of these spirits, because it was believed that they could tell anyone who asked the names of their destined marriage partners.

Of all folklore, ghost stories must be the commonest. It sometimes seems that not only every town and village but every street in Clwyd has its own ghost story. I have a file full of accounts of hauntings from the county, many told to me personally by witnesses. There is enough material, in fact, to make a second volume. For this reason I have limited the ghost stories I tell in this chapter to some of the older, more traditional tales from the county.

And I begin with the most famous from Clwyd, an incident which took place about a hundred yards from where I sit writing this and caused such a sensation at the time that it was even reported in *The Times* newspaper. Although the bulk of the story involves an allegedly true sighting, much of the incidental detail surrounding it has passed into folklore, and I believe it deserves its place here. It is the tale of 'The Golden Spectre of Goblin Hill'.

The Golden Spectre of Goblin Hill

Bryn-yr-ellyllon (*Hill of the Goblins*) was the name given to the hill which rises to the east of Mold on the way to the hamlet of Pentre towards Buckley. It once had a strong reputation for being haunted, a reputation which was apparently proved well founded when a woman encountered a terrifying apparition there in the year 1830.

The woman was a respected farmer's wife returning to her farm from Mold market one late afternoon just as dusk was creeping in. The approach up the hill to Pentre was then heavily wooded and at that time of day clothed in deep shadow. As she ascended Bryn-yr-ellyllon her horse began to whicker nervously and then the farm wife noticed that the woods to her right seemed somehow to be illuminated, as if from within. She wondered whether a fire had started in the copse, for the trees glowed with a golden light. Suddenly, out of the wood strode a huge figure, a giant of a man clad in ancient armour. The weird golden light shone in a halo all around him and the woman cried out in fear as he passed before her. Paying her no heed he stamped by and up to a mound situated on the opposite side of the road. Before the woman's astonished eyes the phantom seemed to stride straight into the tumulus and to descend into the heart of it. The golden light was immediately extinguished.

The farm wife sat aghast for a few moments, and then, impressed with what she had witnessed, she turned her horse about and returned quickly to Mold, there to tell the Vicar, the Rev. Charles Butler Clough, of her experience. The Vicar listened to her story with amazement but did not doubt her veracity. He took down her statement in writing and got two persons to witness it. He then set about trying to discover whether there was any rational explanation for the woman's adventure. He soon found that the ancient tumulus, named Tomen-yr-ellyllon (*Mound of the Goblins*), was regarded as a haunted spot by the locals, and was a place children avoided. An old man who lived nearby, Huw of the Pentre, told him many tales of a spectre seen there, which he referred to as Brenin yr Allt, or 'the King of the Hillside'.

Further research revealed that three other sightings of the golden ghost had been recorded in the previous century. Nancy

A child's scrawl marks the stone plaque commemorating the finding of the Bryn yr Ellyllon treasure.

was the name of one of the witnesses, a girl who saw the spectre standing on the mound when fetching home some cows one moonlit night. Fourteen years later she saw it again whilst trying to escort home her drunken husband from Buckley. A dressmaker who encountered the phantom at about the same time was so terrified by the apparition that she went mad for seven years afterwards.

"It was," she said, "glittering and shining in gold".

These stories may all have been lost to obscurity were it not for a fantastic coincidence which took place just three years after the farm wife's sighting. In 1833 the mound was broken into by some men engaged on widening the road. It was found to contain a Bronze Age cairn in the centre of which lay a crude tomb consisting of four slabs of rough-hewn rock. When the uppermost slab was lifted there was discovered within a huge skeleton, which crumbled away almost instantly to dust on exposure to the air. It was surrounded all about by hundreds of little amber beads, which had once presumably belonged to some article of clothing since rotted. But most startling and dramatic of all was that the upper part of the skeleton was covered by a great piece of gold, beautifully worked and of the finest quality.

185

The amber beads were scooped up by bystanders as souvenirs and carried away. One man, in attempt to prove to himself that they were amber, placed a pile of them on a shovel and put them in the fire. When they melted away he felt pleased with his deduction. The gold ornament suffered greatly, too, as pieces were torn off by eager, greedy hands. Many of the wedding rings handed down to generations of Mold women have been made from the melted down gold from Bryn-yr-ellyllon. Fortunately, most of the ornament, which was firstly described as a breastplate for a horse but now recognised as a cape for a man of great importance, was saved and restored. It still remains the single biggest piece of prehistoric worked gold found anywhere in Europe and it has pride of place in the British Museum in London.

The slabs from the tomb found their way into various stone walls, and the top one became the first of the steps up the Bailey Hill in the centre of Mold. It is said ill luck proceeded the people who had vandalised the site and taken away material from it. There is a story about an old woman who passed by the tumulus soon after it had been opened and found a few of the amber beads lying scattered on the grass. Delighted, she took them home to her young daughter, and made them into a necklace for her. However, that very night the sounds of stamping feet echoed around their cottage, the door was repeatedly knocked upon and the windows rapped, but with no-one visible to account for it. The child became greatly frightened and the woman realised that a ghost was at work. Reluctantly, she took the amber beads from around her daughter's neck and ventured back out into the cold dark night. She trudged to where the Tomen-yr-ellyllon lay silent in the dark and she threw the beads at its base.

"There," she said, "you have back your beads. Now leave us in peace!"

They were troubled no more that night. Today, Tomen-yr-ellyllon has been flattened and a house stands upon it. To commemmorate its presence, however, a stone plaque was cemented into the wall. It is rather inaccurate in some of its facts and makes the interesting suggestion that the skeleton found in the tomb belonged to none other than "Benlli Gawr, a British Prince", but as you and I know the wicked giant Benlli was burnt to a crisp by the power of St Cynhafal a few miles to the west at Loggerheads (see the 'Monsters' chapter).

The Headless Woman

Once upon a time many goblins must have lived at Mold, because not only was there a Goblin Hill near the town but also a Goblin Well. Ffynnon-yr-ellyllon was situated by the side of the road at Maes Garmon on the outskirts of the town, issuing from a tiny arched cell enclosed in a grove of trees. It has since been destroyed by road widening.

Although the Goblin Well was a pretty place to view in daylight it was a place to be avoided at night, for it was haunted by a fearsome bwbach (*evil spirit*). After sundown the road was deserted for no-one would risk passing the well. Well, no-one that is bar one young man. This was a youth who worked at the nearby lead mines at Waen (now called Gwernaffield). He had a girlfriend who was a barmaid at an inn in Mold and his only means of visiting her was to use that road. He didn't get out of the mine until dusk and it was well into the night before he made his journey home. Although he would always feel a shiver of anticipation as he drew near to Ffynnon-yr-ellyllon, nothing ever appeared to frighten him, and so he began to grow confident that the well wasn't haunted after all.

Then, one night as he made his way home from the pub, he saw that for the first time he was not alone on the road. A tall white figure stood some distance ahead, apparently waiting for him to catch up. The stranger turned out to be a woman, dressed all in white, a hood over her head.

"Ah, at last," said a silvery voice from within the hood, "I hope you don't mind my waiting for you, but I was so frightened walking this road alone. You know the Goblin Well is supposed to be haunted, don't you?"

"Yes, yes, I did," replied the young man. "I've never seen anything, though."

The young man and the woman in white began to proceed along the road, and they soon drew opposite the haunted well.

"I don't suppose you happen to have a pick and shovel about you, do you?" asked the white lady. "Ah, but I see that you haven't. Could you fetch some by any chance? You see, there's a fabulous treasure buried beneath the well..."

"Is there? I've never heard that," said the young man, and he decided to take a closer look at his strange companion. He peered into the hood to see her face, but nothing but blackness stared back. The white lady continued, however:

"Oh, yes, there's a very great treasure. I was sacrificed and buried with it, you see, and if you could retrieve the necklace I used to wear I would be particularly pleased because it would help fasten my head back onto my neck." And she threw back her hood — to reveal nothing. Her head was missing!

"Waaaaaaaah!" screamed the young man (or something very similar) and he ran off up the road as fast his legs would carry him. Behind him, the bwbach changed its shape into a fierce spark of fire and it chased after him. The spark bumped and butted up against the young man's breeches as he tore along, and he shrieked and wailed all the way to his cottage door, which he slammed behind him causing the bwbach to blister the wood. The poor young man leapt into bed, and pulled the covers over his head. He lay there all night, trembling, a rowan branch clutched in his hand. By morning he had decided that he had better find himself a girlfriend in Gwernaffield.

The Skull

One of Clwyd's oldest inhabited houses is Ffagnallt Hall at Rhes-y-cae on Halkyn Mountain. The hall has an occupant almost as old as itself — an ancient skull which grins out of a glass fronted box on a ledge in the hallway. The legend which is attached to this strange artefact is as follows:

In the time of Henry I, a hero of the Welsh people was on the run from the English and he gained sanctuary at Ffagnallt Hall, the home of his sister. He was led in by the lord of the house, his sister's husband, and was made to feel welcome. However, during the welcoming feast, he suddenly sprang up, declaring his cup poisoned. The lord of the manor laughed cruelly, for indeed the cup was poisoned — there was a price on the fugitive's head and he intended to claim it. The hero cursed the treacherous lord, and then begged his sister, innocent of the crime, to remove his head from his body and to keep it in the hall in a place of honour to remind the world of the dreadful deed. At that point, he said, his vengeance would cease. Then, the hero died.

The hero's sister and the whole court were horrified by the act,

Ffagnallt Hall.

but the wicked lord gleefully cut off the hero's head and got a bag full of gold for it at Chester. However, things then went bad for him, for, after burying the remains of her brother's body at Basingwerk Abbey, his wife left him, and so did each member of his retinue, one by one. He eventually died in madness, broken in the empty hall. His son then took possession, and his retinue and his mother were reinstated. He removed his uncle's head, now a fleshless skull, from its spike on Chester city gate, and placed it in the hall. From then on, the hall prospered.

However, if at any time in the future the skull was removed from Ffagnallt the hero's curse was renewed. The hall was immediately thrown into pandemonium, with moaning sounds filling the empty corridors, windows and doors being crashed open and closed, shadowy shapes appearing in all parts of the house and bad luck falling on every occupant. Great care was taken therefore to ensure that the skull never left the hall even for a moment. One day last century, however, the skull *was* removed. A young serving maid had received a very severe telling off by the lady of the hall for neglecting to dust the books in the library, and on her afternoon off she was made to stay in and do the job properly. She was in a very bad mood. At this time the skull had been placed out of the way on top of one of the bookcases, and the angry young maid couldn't help thinking that it was to blame for all the dust. She decided to do something about it.

She fetched a step ladder, placed it against the bookcase and climbed to the top. There she found the skull, crumbling away, covered in spiders' nests.

"Ugh!" she said. "Horrible thing."

Gingerly, she picked it up, wrapped it in her apron, and took it outside. She glanced around to make sure no-one was watching and then, with all her might, she lobbed the hero's skull right into the centre of the farmyard pond. She gave a satisfied smile, and feeling much better for taking her bad temper out on something she returned to her dusting.

That night, terrible shrieks were heard throughout the house, and bumps and crashes resounded in every room. The hall's owners woke up in a fright and, putting on their nightgowns, went downstairs to try and find out what was causing all the commotion. They caught sight of something splashing about in the pond outside, and they went to investigate. A ghostly white figure with a pale face and straggly hair emerged from the pond and came towards them. The owners backed away... and then they saw that it was just the serving maid. She appeared to be sleepwalking and was muttering to herself unintelligibly. To her bosom she was clutching the skull.

Quite bemused, the owners helped the delirious girl up to her room, but they dared not try and remove the skull, for she became quite fierce if they tried. After a day or two, the maid recovered from her trance and the first thing she did was to return the skull to its accustomed place above the bookcase. She told her employers that she had been woken in the middle of the night by "fingers dripping wet" and "shadowy forms" who forced her, she hardly knew why, to retrieve the skull from where she had thrown it in the pond.

Murder Will Out

One dark, misty night in the latter years of the 18th Century an excise man collecting rents from farms on Mynydd Hiraethog lost his way on his return journey to Denbigh. The fog closed in around him and he began to shiver in the cold. He could scarcely see beyond the nose of his horse as it edged its way nervously forward, but he could hear the muffled splashing from beneath its hoofs which told him that he had entered boggy ground. He gave up all hope of reaching Denbigh that night and began to doubt whether he could find any lodging, either. Through the gloom, however, he shortly detected a dim light some way ahead, and he nudged his mount towards it. The light came from a guttering candle in the window of a little stone cottage situated adjacent to a ruined mill. The excise man quickly dismounted and hammered on the door.

For some time he received no reply, but eventually a little old man came to the door and glowered at the excise man furiously.

"Who are you disturbing my rest? I receive no visitors here," he snapped. "Be off with you!"

When the excise man asked whether he could lodge there for the night, the cottage owner was quite taken aback. No-one ever asked him for lodgings, for he was loathed and feared in the district. He was a well-known miser, known to possess a hoard of money the earning of which was unaccountable with his lowly situation. What's more, his home, Mill House Cottage, had a reputation for being haunted. But all this was unknown to the excise man, who pressed his case with the old man and offered him enough silver to tempt him.

"Very well," said the miser, "stable your horse next door and you may use the room downstairs. I am returning to bed!" And he stomped upstairs. The excise man soon settled himself down in his temporary accommodation, ate a little bread and cheese which he had left in his saddle bag, and he tried to sleep.

He had hardly began to doze off when something suddenly made him open his eyes. In one corner of the room stood a shadow. At first he thought it was the old man creeping around, but the shade was far too tall. The figure was wearing some kind of long gown, like a Jew's gaberdine, and he noticed too that he had long hair and a prominent nose. The shadow passed by the excise man's bed and seemed to beckon. Then it left the room.

Full of curiosity, the excise man roused himself and followed. To his surprise, he found the door still bolted from the inside, but he opened it and went out. The shadow stood in the yard and again seemed to beckon. The excise man followed. The figure led him to a boggy patch of ground at the rear of the yard and there — vanished.

"A ghost..." murmured the excise man. He shuddered, but

went to investigate the patch of ground where the phantom had vanished. It looked as if it had been recently disturbed. He marked it with a stick, so that he could recognise it the next morning, and then returned to his bed.

At dawn, the excise man rose quietly, left the house without waking its owner and led his horse away. In the daylight it was not long before he recognised his location. He was near Llanynys (*Church of the Island*), a village which in those days was surrounded by marshland. It was not many miles to Denbigh and he rode there at a gallop. At once he contacted the local constable and told him of his strange adventure the previous night. Armed with spades they returned to Mill House Cottage and they dug at the spot the excise man had indicated with a stick. Six feet down, they found the decomposing body of a Jew.

It did not take long to get the truth out of the old miser. He confessed that he had killed the Jew. He had been a rich merchant, with a considerable amount of gold on his person. He had arrived at his cottage door on a night similar to that the excise man had been lost in and in a similar state, begging for lodging. The miser had not been able to resist taking the gold for himself, aware that no-one else knew of the rich Jew's existence.

The miser was hanged at Denbigh at the next assizes. Mill House Cottage crumbled away, for no-one would live there again.

A Cry in the Dark

It was a bitter night. A freezing wind howled across the moors around the village of Cerrigydrudion and the frost lay thick on the windowpanes. It was the sort of night self-respecting folk kept abed and wrapped themselves in warm covers. It was also just the sort of night a doctor finds himself called from his slumbers to attend an emergency. On this particular night it was the lot of Dr Davies to be awoken by a cry for assistance.

He stirred and moaned. He had heard a voice below his window calling his name.

"Dr Davies!" it had cried. "You are needed at Craigeirchan farm!"

Craigeirchan farm lay miles away across the Hiraethog Moors.

It was not easily accessible at the best of times, but on a night such as this, it would be madness to attempt the journey. Dr Davies therefore did not rouse himself. He rolled over on his side.

However, when the voice called urgently a second time, the doctor could not ignore it, and reluctantly, he dragged himself from his bed and he went to the window. He scraped the frost from the glass and stared out, but he could see no-one there. Confused, he returned to bed.

But then the voice cried out again. The tone was desperate. This time, Dr Davies roused himself properly. He could not shirk his responsibility, he decided. He opened the window and called out: "Very well, I shall come!"

Soon, he was on his way, guiding his horse along the rocky path which led the miles to Craigeirchan. It was blood-numbingly cold and the wind buffetted the poor doctor and his trembling horse unmercifully. Although he had been confused by not seeing the owner to the voice which had called him from his bed, Dr Davies was not so surprised by the fact that he could not see anyone out on the track before him. Welsh farm lads are nimble and can easily outstrip a rider by taking short-cuts across the moor.

After what seemed like an age, the doctor finally reached Craigeirchan. The whole house was illuminated. This told the doctor at once that there was sickness there, and his services were required. He dismounted, grabbed his black bag from where it hung at the saddle and hurried inside without even knocking. The distraught family he found within were overjoyed to see him, but also amazed. The lady of the house was on the verge of becoming a mother, and there were complications. However, they had not risked sending out anyone for a doctor on such a fearful night.

"But somebody called for me to come here," spluttered the astonished Dr Davies. "I distinctly heard a voice, three times!"

The family could offer no explanation, and there was no time to discuss the issue further, for the expectant mother urgently requried attention. One thing proved certain, however. Whoever, or whatever, had cried for help under the doctor's window that night, had saved the life not only of a young mother, but of a baby, too.

Valley of Death

Midway between Corwen and Cerrigydrudion, just off the A5 trunk road into Gwynedd, there is situated a little bridge, called Pont y Glyn. It spans a deep wooded chasm gouged out by the fast flowing River Ceirw. In days gone by, this valley formed a route through North Wales to Caernarfon and was later replaced by a well-used road which skirted its edge and crossed over at Pont y Glyn. The present A5 which clips the bridge is a remnant of this ancient road. Today, thousands of holidaymakers drive past the spectacular gorge, unaware that they are missing one of the most beautiful valleys in North Wales, and also one of the most mysterious.

Its tree-shrouded depths made the perfect setting for ambushes, and was a favourite place for bandits to waylay lonely travellers. So many people have met untimely ends in this lovely gorge that at night it is said to be crowded with their ghosts. The spirits of both the murder victims and their killers drift among the trees and patrol the bridge. Many a traveller crossing over Pont y Glyn has said good evening to someone crossing the other way, only to watch him disappear, and one man on horseback had to rein in his horse when a rider on the other side refused to halt, and then passed straight through him, horse and all!

Of all the spirits haunting Pont y Glyn, the strangest bore the name Ysbryd Ystrad Fawr, or *Spirit of Ystrad Fawr*, Ystrad Fawr being a farmhouse on the outskirts of nearby Llangwm. This spirit could transform itself into a variety of strange guises, including a huge dog gnawing a bone, a giant turkey "with its tail spread out like a spinning wheel", or sometimes just a fiery glow in the bushes. Ysbryd Ystrad Fawr was possibly responsible for the extraordinary apparition described in the "Giant Phantoms" section of the 'Monsters' chapter. A man encountered a lady in traditional Welsh costume, sitting on a pile of stones at one end of the bridge, who stood up, began to walk away, and as she did so grew to monstrous proportions.

A Tapping at the Glass

If you have ever visited the village of Marford in Wrexham Maelor you will have been immediately struck by the peculiar architecture of the majority of the houses. The village was largely rebuilt in the early years of the last century by the Trevor family of Trevalyn Hall, and the houses were all built to a unique design, a design which incorporated the adornment of every house with a cross. Everywhere one looks in Marford one is faced with crucifixes. Crosses are set in at least one wall of every house, and some have crucifix-shaped windows. And they are all there for a purpose — they are there to keep at bay the wandering ghost of the Lady Blackbird.

In September 1713, Madam Margaret Blackbourne of Rofft Hall, now replaced by what is called Roft Castle, was murdered by her husband, George Blackbourne, the Steward of Marford and Hosely. George Blackbourne was a drunkard and a womaniser. One night, of many nights, he returned home late, the worse for drink, and his tearful wife stood at the top of the stairs and demanded to know with whom he had been and whether he had been unfaithful to her. There was a furious row, and then a scream was heard, and a loud thump. Then silence. The servants were too in fear of their master to investigate, and they stayed in their beds. The following morning, the body of Margaret Blackbourne was found, its neck broken, slumped at the foot of the staircase. The magistrates turned a blind eye to the incident, and a verdict of misadventure was brought by the coroner. Six months later George Blackbourne found himself a young wife.

But he was to receive no peace with his new bride. From the night of his nuptials, the corpse of his murdered wife shifted uneasily in its tomb and then clawed its way out and stalked off to Rofft Hall. Every night, Margaret's body would walk through Marford to plague her husband and his young bride. The villagers would always know when she was passing, for she would stop at each house and would tap pathetically at the glass. Her pale face would peer through with dead eyes, her hair awry. Then she would proceed to roam through the corridors of her former home, moaning horribly.

George moved to Trevalyn Hall at nearby Rossett, but his

dead wife followed him there, too. Eventually, an archdeacon was called in to lay the spirit, but he was only partly successful. Although Margaret's corpse was at last laid to rest, it seems her spirit continued to roam, for even into this century, villagers at Marford have claimed to see her face at their windows, to have heard the tapping at the glass.

The story of poor Margaret Blackbourne has passed into legend, and her history is largely forgotten. Her name has been corrupted, so that she is now known as Lady Blackbird, the Ghost of Marford.

The Scrumpers' Fright

When Squire Griffiths of Foelas Hall at Pentrefoelas died, everyone in the village breathed a sigh of relief. In those days of the late 18th Century the local squire ruled village and countryside with a rod of iron and his law went. The Squire Griffiths was not known either for a generous nature or charitable disposition and immediately after his death it was a case of "while the cat's away, the mice will play". A couple of workmen on his estate decided to take advantage of the general confusion before the new squire took his place and one evening crept into the Squire Griffiths' previously well-guarded orchard to steal some apples.

As they made their way between the silent apple trees in the darkness, the workmen whispered to each other nervously, but with a growing sense of boldness at their daring. They chose a tall, particularly well-laden tree, climbed it, and, laughing and joking, began filling their sacks with the ripe, crisp apples. Then one of the workmen gave a squawk of fright. He pointed to the ground. Below them, passing directly beneath the tree, they could see a very familiar three-cornered hat.

"It's the squire!" hissed the workman, terrified.

"Can't be, the squire's dead," pointed out his fellow, logically. They looked again. Squire Griffiths glared up.

It was Squire Griffiths' ghost!

Screaming wildly, they leapt out of the tree and ran for dear life. They charged out of the orchard and on towards their homes at Bryn Coch. But there — horror of horrors — they found the

Squire waiting for them. He was leaning upon his staff in the middle of the road and frowning darkly. The workmen shrieked, and ran off home another way.

Squire Griffiths was never seen again. But then no-one tried stealing apples from his orchard again.

The Exorcist

One bitterly cold, stormy night in the 1840's an old beggar came to the door of Tŷ Mawr, a large farmhouse at Bryneglwys, and pleaded for shelter and something to eat. But the daughters of the house, who answered the door, laughed at his shabby appearance and scorned the poor man. They sent him away.

"You will repent your conduct to me!" swore the beggar, and, pulling his threadbare coat about him, he went off across the yard, shivering in the cold. The next morning, his body was found lying beneath a hedge bordering one of the farm's fields. He had frozen to death. Two weeks later, the hauntings at Tŷ Mawr Farm began.

A dreadful wailing shrieked through the house at night. Heavy footsteps ascended the staircase and dragged around the empty corridors, as doors opened and closed of their own accord. A strange mixture of ashes and milk was found every morning spread all over the floors. After a couple of days, the grinning face of the old beggar man began to appear at the windows, and invisible, bony fingers began to pluck and pinch the servant girls, never giving them a moment's rest, until they were tired of their lives. Clearly someone had to be found who could lay the ghost. The most famous exorcist in the district was a minister from Graianrhyd near Llanarmon-yn-Iâl, the Rev. Griffiths. They pleaded with him to come and free them of the spirit which plagued them.

The Rev. Griffiths came to the house and in the kitchen he drew two circles on the floor. He stood in one of these, and then, in a loud voice, he charged the spirit to appear. Peals of sinister laughter answered this charge, and a bible flew across the room. Then, the kitchen door crashed open and a giant black bull roared in, placing its front hoofs in the circle on the floor opposite the Rev. Griffiths. The family, who had been cowering behind the exorcist ran screaming out of the room. The Rev. Griffiths did not flinch. He commanded the spirit to appear in its proper guise, and its shape shimmered and took the form of the beggar man. Then, the Rev. Griffiths began to read the words of exorcism.

At once, the beggar's ghost returned to the form of the black bull. A terrible struggle of wills took place as the Rev. Griffiths desperately tried to lay the spirit of the vengeful beggar. The spirit changed into a variety of animal shapes as the minister performed the exorcism. It became a tiger, a mastiff, a black pig, but becoming smaller and smaller as the exorcism proceeded. Eventually, it was so small that it took the form of a spider. The Rev. Griffiths pounced forward and scooped the spider into an old tobacco tin he had in his pocket. This he took out onto the moors, where he weighted it with stones and dropped it into a bog.

Following this adventure, the Rev. Griffiths was called back to Bryneglwys to perform an exorcism at another farm in the district, Ffridd Farm. The dairy at Ffridd Farm was haunted by a poltergeist, which would smash the dishes and throw filth into the butter churns. Surrounded by a crowd of gawping villagers, the local priest had tried to exorcise it and had failed. The spirit had waved a woman's bonnet in his face as a mark of contempt and then had continued with its destructive behaviour worse than before. The Rev. Griffiths wasn't prepared to be put off so easily, however. He performed the same exorcism he had used at Tŷ Mawr, drawing two circles on the floor of the dairy and loudly charging the spirit to show itself. A great black lion materialised in the middle of the circle. The exorcist joined wills with the spirit, and eventually he managed to make it become a fly. This he snapped up in another tobacco box and he carried it away.

The other famous exorcism which the Rev. Griffiths is known to have performed took place at Llandegla. The Rectory became haunted by a violent spirit, which would throw objects around the house and even clods of earth at passers-by on the road outside. The Rev. Griffiths had a terrific struggle subduing the spirit, but eventually managed to make it shrink down to the form of a fly, and, whipping another trusty tobacco box from his pocket, he imprisoned it. It buzzed about furiously inside the tin, but could not escape. The Rev. Griffiths carried it down to the river at the bottom of the hill, and there buried it under a large flat stone beneath the bridge. He charged the spirit to remain

An angry spirit was entombed beneath the ancient bridge at Llandegla.

there until the top branches of a little hazel tree which grew on the bank reached the height of the bridge.

To keep the spirit trapped, the local children used to trim the tree's branches every year. However, since this custom ceased many years ago, and the tree has grown taller than the little bridge, it can be assumed that the spirit has escaped and is causing trouble elsewhere.

Plas Teg

Clwyd's most famous (or should I say infamous?) haunted house is Plas Teg, *the Fair Mansion*, which stands beside the busy dual carriageway between Wrexham and Mold at Pontblyddyn. Built in 1610 by John Trevor, of the same family which built **Trevalyn Hall** at Rossett, it is a grand, square, beautiful house, recently restored by interior designer Cornelia Bayley. For many years it stood derelict and certainly took on a sinister aspect at nightfall. Many are the ghost tales told about it.

Phantom horsemen patrol the old avenue leading to the door of Clwyd's most famous haunted house, Plas Teg.

The best known concerns a young girl, daughter of the house, who was tragically killed sometime in the 17th Century while attempting to escape an enforced marriage. Some say that she was a daughter of the Dacre family who once lived in the Hall, others she was Dorothy Trevor, youngest daughter of the first owner. There are many different versions of the same story. When broken down to a common plot, the story explains how the girl fell in love with a local farmer's son, and agreed to elope with him the night before her planned marriage to an old dignitary. But she never turned up.

On an impulse, she had stolen some of the family jewels, and before going on to her rendezvous had attempted to hide them in the well, to be collected later. However, she stumbled and fell in and drowned. Her decomposing body was found two weeks later, just a couple of days after her lover had hanged himself from the tree where they had agreed to meet, driven to despair by his uncertainty as to his beloved's fate and the constant fingers of accusation that had been pointed at him. After such a tragic history, it is only to be expected that the spirit of the poor girl —

The Jacobean staircase, Plas Teg.

and also that of her lover — began to haunt the house and grounds.

Even today, the tragic lovers make their presence known. Feminine footsteps have often been heard by Cornelia Bayley tripping around the second floor, although she has also heard much heavier, masculine tread. One night, heavy steps crashed down the stairs and a fierce hammering sounded at her bedroom door. But, of course, the perpetrator could not be found. The bedroom traditionally said to be the haunted one, now called 'The Twin Poster', still has a creepy atmosphere about it. I guessed it to be the haunted one as soon as I walked into it; it seemed to possess a tense, claustrophobic atmosphere which is hard to describe. It is said that strange glowing white lights have been seen passing by the window of this room when the house has been deserted.

The main entrance way, now a grove of lime trees bisected by the dual carriageway and leading nowhere, also has a reputation for being haunted. Standing at one end of the drive there was once a lodge, the home of the gatekeeper. However, the last gatekeeper saw some apparition here so distressing that he killed himself soon after, and the lodge was never occupied again. The same apparition may have been seen a few years ago by a member of a party of ramblers who passed Plas Teg one twilight. He had been straggling behind, but suddenly ran up to his companions in a state of shock, but would not say what he had seen.

Since the dual carriageway cuts through the original entrance, it is not surprising that the road too is haunted. Misty white shapes have been known to run out in front of motorists, causing them to swerve and brake, thinking that they have run over a living person. Even more mysterious, for there is no story to account for their presence, are the phantom horsemen who patrol the highway. I have read old accounts of the shadowy horsemen who torment poachers and pursue riders before vanishing mysteriously, but I was astonished to discover that, according to the locals anyway, they still haunt the district. They make their presence known mainly at dusk in September and October, and one or two sightings at least seem to occur every year.

With so much supernatural activity taking place at Plas Teg, you might believe that there could be nowhere in Clwyd more scary. But the old hermit who once slept within the ruined walls of Rhuddlan Castle would not agree with you. In the little book of *Welsh Legends* published by J. Bacock in 1802, the hermit accosts a nightbound traveller and tells him:

"Such groans have met my ears! — such sights my eyes! — and screams and riotous laughs mingled with the wind that whistled through the broken arches of the courts! — e'en now, the sweat of terror dews my brow, and languid beats my heart."

The tale he has to tell is a fabulous one, epic in quality, recounted in true Gothic prose, of which the above is a comparatively restrained example. And yet it is not recorded anywhere outside those pages, and so is virtually unknown. It is also my favourite of all the Clwyd folk tales. It could have appeared in the Devil Chapter, the Monsters chapter, the Fairies chapter or the Witchcraft and Sorcery chapter. But I have left its inclusion until now — the final story in this book. It is called "The Warrior Knight of the Blood Red Plume".

The Warrior Knight of the Blood Red Plume

After centuries of conflict, hope for peace had filled the hearts of Welshmen. At last, friendly relations had been made between the kingdoms of North and South Wales. Erilda, beautiful daughter of Sir Rhyswick of Rhuddlan Castle, King of North Wales, was to marry Morvern, Prince of South Wales, and all hostilities between the two nations had ceased.

However, deep, deep in the blackest pit of hell, a plot was being hatched to foil this chance for happiness. A demon charged with stirring up murderous intentions and wars, roused himself from his ancient slumber and rose to the upper world, intent on evil.

The Princess Erilda shivered inside her heavy fur robes and reined in her horse. The Royal Hunt, with whom she had been riding, charged past her, and her father, Sir Rhyswick, shouted some word of encouragement to her and grinned through his grey beard. But Erilda could only smile weakly in return. Ever since the announcement of her betrothal to Morvern, Prince of

Powys, a relief, a joy, had entered the hearts of her fellow courtiers, but she could not quite share their optimism. Although she was proud of the part she was to play in the unification of Wales, she could only feel trepidation at the thought of her approaching wedding. The first time she would meet Morvern would be the night before the ceremony and her heart was heavy that she was to marry a man who was a stranger to her. Sighing, she urged on her horse to follow the Royal Hunt, which had proceeded ahead of her into the forest.

When Erilda entered the forest, however, she could see no sign of the royal party, and nor could she hear the sounds of the chase; the pounding of hoofs, the cries, the huntsmen's horns. All was silent. Once more, Erilda felt an unnatural chill caress her flesh. She galloped ahead through the trees, but soon the path petered out and there was nothing to indicate that the hunt had been that way. She raised herself up in her saddle.

"Father! Father!" she called, but she received no reply. She decided that they must have broken cover some short distance from where they had first entered and that she had missed them, but when she wheeled her horse around to return back, she found all trace of the path had vanished. The ancient trees enclosed her tightly. A darkness was creeping in around her and a fog was rising from the ground. A sudden indefinable fear clutched at Erilda's heart, and she quickly dug her spurs into her horse's flanks. She galloped back through the trees, in the direction she thought she had come, but all seemed unfamiliar. The darkness grew and the fog clung clammy to her skin. Malevolent eyes seemed to glare at her from behind every tree and the swirling mist formed hideous faces before her eyes. In a panic, she forced her horse to race hither and thither through the forest, caring not which direction she took, filled only with the urgent need to escape its clutches.

Suddenly, her horse reared up and she was thrown. It galloped away, leaving the princess alone, lying bruised upon the forest floor. Above her loomed a shadow, which approached her through the fog. It reached out for her. Erilda cried out in terror.

"Fear not, my lady," spoke a deep and gentle voice, "I mean only to assist you. I am Wertwold, the Warrior Knight of the Blood Red Plume, and, my lady, I am at your service."

The princess was raised up into the arms of the knight and she gazed into a proud and beautiful face, strong and dark-eyed. And then she lost conciousness.

"Tortured spirits in yon castle roam..." The majestic ruin of Rhuddlan Castle overlooks the River Clwyd.

The Warrior Knight of the Blood Red Plume entered the forecourt of Rhuddlan Castle to a clamorous reception. For hours the frantic King and his courtiers had searched the forest for the princess without success, and there had been serious fears for her safety. But across the saddle of his black horse, this mysterious knight, clad all in black bar the great plume of blood red feathers cresting his helmet, had borne her, unconscious but unhurt. Erilda was taken to her room and when she awoke she was found to be no worse for her terrifying experience. Her rescuer was taken in ceremony into the great hall and a feast was prepared in his honour. But he declined to eat anything, and although he was the model of courtesy he would answer no questions regarding himself. At length, he asked to take his leave of the princess and he was shown to Erilda's room. Erilda, too, was full of curiosity regarding her handsome saviour. Despite his powerful mien, there was an extraordinary gentleness in his manner and much sadness behind his eyes. But he would shake his head at any question she asked him about himself and he would say nothing.

"I must leave you now, princess," he said at last, and rose to go.

"No, please stay," Erilda begged. Wertwold got to his knees

beside her bed and removed from his finger a ring set with a dark stone. He handed it to her. It felt warm at the touch and glowed with an inner fire.

"If you ever wish to see me again, my princess, hold my ring between your fingers and call for me. I shall come."

He swept from the room.

In the days that followed, the Princess Erilda could do nothing but think of the dark knight. His mystery haunted her. His face seemed to float before her gaze, and when she closed her eyes his eyes seemed to be before her, staring deep into her soul. The memory of his presence filled her heart, and her flesh seemed to feel about it his strong embrace. At last, she took his ring from where she had locked it in her jewellery box and she clasped it in her palm.

"Wertwold..." she whispered. She felt a hand on her shoulder and turned to find that it was he. His dark eyes seemed to swallow her up.

"My lady," he murmered, "now I know that you love me as much as I love you."

He held her to him and kissed her. Erilda felt that her life had waited only for this moment. She knew that she was indeed in love with him.

"Will you marry me, Erilda?"

Erilda staggered back from the knight.

"No, no, I cannot... I must marry Morvern, Prince of Powys."

Werwold turned away.

"Then you condemn me to an existence of unbearable agony. You see, my lady, I am accursed! I beg you, do not ask me of my history or my past shame, suffice for you to know that I am cursed with an eternity of torture unless I can find a pure hearted spirit like yourself to love me, to absolve my sins. You must marry me. If you love me."

"But I cannot, I cannot!" wailed the distraught Erilda. "It would break my father's heart to leave him."

Wertwold moved to the window and threw it open. A climbing winter rose bobbed against the glass. The knight gestured for Erilda to join him and there he showed her two rose blossoms, one fresh, alive, the other, yellowing, nearly dead.

"If you were forced to pick one of these blooms, Erilda — which would you feel less cruel to pick?"

Erilda understood. She sighed. Werwold took her in his arms.

"I shall come for you tomorrow at midnight. Tell no-one of our plans. They would stop us. For now, goodnight."

He kissed her, and was gone. The following evening, Prince Morvern and his company arrived at the castle. From her casement Erilda watched the party enter. In the middle of the company rode the Prince in high estate, but from her position high above them he seemed small, and insignificant, beneath her notice. So obsessed had she been with the Warrior Knight of the Blood Red Plume that all thought of her impending marriage to the Prince had been forgotten. Tomorrow morning she would be expected to stand in the chapel alongside him, making her marriage vows, and in so doing uniting in peace the nation of Wales. But now nothing seemed to her worthy of her attention but her love for the mysterious knight who had rescued her those few scant days ago in the forest. The thought of her father's despair at her elopement she forbid to enter her mind.

At midnight, Wertwold appeared in her room. He took her face in his hands and smiled upon her, his eyes entrancing her. Any doubts Erilda had felt at her impending flight evaporated. But then into her hand, the knight pressed a dagger.

"But... why?"

"Just in case, my love... just in case," Wertwold murmered encouragingly, and then took her by the arm and guided her from the room. They flitted silently through the empty corridors and down the steep spiral stairs to the open portcullis. But as they passed under it a cry went up from within.

"We are discovered!" yelled Wertwold. "I have a coracle moored on the river — it will take us to our new home. Run!"

He grabbed Erilda's arm and dragged her swiftly towards the River Clwyd. Behind them torches flared in the castle, and a cloaked figure left the shadows and came after them across the drawbridge, hot in pursuit. Nothing now filled Erilda's head except the desperate need to escape with her new-found lover. She took one glance over her shoulder as she ran for the river, and saw the cloaked figure scarcely a yard behind her. As they reached the river's edge, her pursuer grabbed her shoulder and attempted to drag her back.

"No!" shrieked the princess in her desperation, and she whirled around and thrust the dagger Wertwold had given her into the cloaked man's body. He uttered a cry and fell at her feet. The cloak slipped from him as he fell — to reveal the aged face of

Sir Rhyswick, King of North Wales. Erilda had murdered her own father!

Erilda screamed with horror. Behind her, Wertwold laughed scornfully.

"Why do you grieve so, girl?" he asked. "You were quite prepared to leave him to suffer long years of misery without you, forever tormented by the thought of your faithlessness. Better that you should have dispatched him quickly, rather than to leave him to such a fate."

Erilda tried to speak, to answer him, but no words came, but her mind screamed over and over, pleading with him to show her now the love he had professed for her, that he himself had engendered in her being. But Wertwold shook his head, seeming to know what was in her mind.

"No, Erilda, I do not love you. I am incapable of love. I am not a man. I am an agent of the Infernal. Gaze upon my true form!"

The knight's face deformed, buckled and turned green. He twitched and shook and suddenly his armour cracked open as his body swelled outward and upward. His skin grew over with scales, his face twisted reptilian and his eyes popped out of his head. His whole form became that of some hideous, fishlike creature, and he bellowed triumphantly. A huge trident grew out of the demon's claw and he plunged it savagely into Erilda's breast, killing her instantly. Contemptuously, he threw her corpse into the foaming waters of the river.

Its evil work completed, the demon slid beneath the waves, and returned to its black lair in Hell. Hours later, the broken body of the wretched Princess Erilda was borne up by the waters of the Clwyd and was sent smashing against the rocks. And now, so the old hermit in the original story tells us:

"from dusky eve until return of morn... tortured spirits in yon castle roam..." as the ghost of the terrified Erilda is pursued by the phantom of the Warrior Knight of the Blood Red Plume round and round the eerie ruins, performing a ghastly scenario forever.

Spirits of the Dead — Bibliography

Rev. Elias Owen, *Welsh Folklore* (Oswestry and Wrexham 1896 & E.P. Publishing 1976).

Rev. Elias Owen, *Old Stone Crosses of the Vale of Clwyd* (London, Oswestry and Wrexham 1886).

Ken Radford, *Tales of North Wales* (Skilton and Shaw 1982).

Marie Trevelyan, *Folklore and Folk Stories of Wales* (Eliot Stock 1909).

Wirt Sikes, *British Goblins* (Sampson Low 1880 & E.P. Publishing 1973).

Welsh Legends (London, for J. Bacock, Paternoster Row, 1802).

M.B. Clough, *Scenes and Stories Little Known* (Mold and London 1861).

Chris Barber, *Mysterious Wales* (Paladin 1982).

Chris Barber, *Ghosts of Wales* (John Jones).

Jane Pugh, *Welsh Ghost, Poltergeists and Demons* (1978).

Thomas Pennant, *A Tour Through Wales* (London 1784).

Maxwell Fraser, *Wales Vol. 2* (Robert Hale Ltd 1952).

Charles Henry Leslie, *Rambles Round Mold* (Mold 1869).

'Penman', *Mold Gleanings* (Chester Chronicle, 1928).

Sydney G. Jarman, *Rosset And Marford* (Wrexham 1909).

Stan Coulter, *The Rhewl* (Corwen Printing 1986).

G.H. Longrigg, *Legends of the Dee* (Liverpool 1901).

Ellis Davies M.A., F.S.A., *The Prehistoric and Roman Remains of Flintshire* (Cardiff 1949).

J. Gwynn Williams M.A., *Witchcraft In 17th Century Flintshire* (Flintshire Historical Society Transactions).

Byegones.

Country Quest.

The Gazette.

The Chronicle.

Clwyd Record Office (Hawarden).

GLOSSARY

Aber	*mouth of river*	Mawr	*great*
Afon	*stream or river*	Melin	*mill*
Allt	*side of a hill*	Moel	*bald, round-topped hill*
Bach	*little*	Mynydd	*mountain*
Bedd	*grave*	Nant	*brook, valley with stream*
Betws	*prayer house*	Newydd	*new*
Bod	*residence*	Pant	*hollow*
Bron	*breast*	Pen	*summit*
Bryn	*hill*	Pentre	*hamlet*
Bwlch	*pass*	Pistyll	*spout*
Cadair	*chair, throne*	Plas	*hall*
Cae	*field*	Pont	*bridge*
Caer	*fort*	Pwll	*pool*
Capel	*chapel*	Rhaeadr	*waterfall*
Carnedd	*heap of stones, cairn*	Rhewl	*the road*
Carreg	*stone*	Rhos	*moor*
Castell	*castle*	Rhyd	*ford*
Cefn	*ridge, back of a hill*	Tan	*under*
Clawdd	*dyke*	Tafarn	*tavern*
Coch	*red*	Tomen	*mound*
Coed	*wood*	Tref	*town*
Craig	*crag*	Twll	*hole*
Croes	*cross*	Twr	*tower*
Dinas	*fortified dwelling*	Tŷ	*house*
Ddôl	*meadow*	Tyddyn	*cottage*
Du	*black*	Uchaf	*highest or more important*
Dŵr	*water*	Y, Yr	*the*
Dyffryn	*valley*	Ym	*in*
Eglwys	*church*	Yn	*in, into, at*
Ffordd	*road or way*	Waen	*uncultivated place*
Ffridd	*mountain pasture*	Wen	*white*
Ffynnon	*well*	Ynys	*island*
Glas	*blue, green*	Ysbyty	*almshouse, hospital*
Glyn	*glen*	Ystrad	*flat vale*
Gwern	*alder-grove*		
Gwyn	*white*		
Hafod	*summer dwelling*		
Hen	*old*		
Hendre	*old or winter dwelling*		
Heol	*street*		
Iâl	*upland country*		
Isaf	*lowest or humblest*		
Llan	*church, village with church*		
Llwyd	*grey, holy*		
Llyn	*lake*		
Llys	*palace*		
Maen	*special stone*		
Maes	*meadow or field*		